White Mother

WHITE

MOTHER

JESSIE BENNETT SAMS

McGraw-Hill Book Company, Inc.

NEW YORK   TORONTO   LONDON

WHITE MOTHER

Library of Congress Catalog Card Number: 57–12911

FIRST EDITION

To Mrs. Rossie Lee, a Southern white woman, whose wise kindness, patience, and understanding helped us to find a new and better way of life; and to little Mingie, my twin sister, who on a hot summer morning ran off in search of work for money to buy us shoes and met this woman with a heart of gold.

Acknowledgment and deepest gratitude is made here to Mr. Edwin Balmer of Sunnyside Lane in Irvington, New York, and his dear wife for their help, encouragement, and inspiration in getting White Mother to press.

White Mother

Veanie was my favorite nickname, and Mingie my sister's, when we were children. Except for a few fictitious names used for reasons that will be obvious, this is a true story as it was lived and remembered by my sister and me, and recorded in its sequence as nearly as I could recall it.

J. B. S.

I

ABOUT ME crowds of happy travelers mill about the gray stone platform. Laughter and chatter rise and fall. The gleaming cars of streamliners glide in and out the great Los Angeles station. Redcaps push clumsy carts piled high with the bright and the drab encumbrances of travel.

From a loudspeaker, a woman dispatcher's voice warns me that the *Spirit of St. Louis* is about to depart. It is the train which is to take me half of my way across the continent on an errand to which I cannot reconcile myself and because of a circumstance which I cannot make myself believe. Yet it prevents my continuing in this time and place.

My fellow travelers see, if they notice me at all, a woman in a tailored beige suit and matching hat who appears calm and casual as she searches a car for her ticketed place. Seat 49. I settle myself and now, in spite of all I can do, my eyes begin to sting again. I open my purse and my fingers touch the folded paper of a telegram. Let it be; too well I know what it says. From the bottom of my purse I take out a carefully wrapped package. I unfold the thin white tissue and spread out a delicate blue organdy handkerchief, worn fragile in its creases. Through a blur of tears I see embroidered "R. L.," and suddenly, as if they had been waiting all these years, the mercies and cruelties of my memories engulf me. . . .

I am a child, a scrawny, black-skinned little girl in a small town in Florida more than thirty years ago.

Mingie, my twin, and I had come out of the stifling shack in which Papa lay in bed, helpless, unable to move more than his hands and his head.

"Veanie," Mingie said to me, "um goin' up town an' fin' us a job an' make some money so we can buy Papa mo' to eat—an' maybe buy us some shoes."

"Don' go out in that hot sun, Mingie," I pleaded. "Don' leave me here by myself with Papa on his bad day."

But Mingie just jumped the two rickety steps into the deep burning sand and trotted off through it on her heels to keep the hot white grains from peppering the tops of her feet. I knew how it felt as I watched her hopping from grassy spot to grassy spot. Jig, Aunt Tiller's old brown dog, lay on one of them, lazy old Jig who was mean when you bothered him. He snapped and caught Mingie's right ankle. She flung herself right into the middle of a scorching sand bed.

I screamed, "Mingie! Did he hurt you?"

Mingie never answered but hopped on until she reached the railroad tracks, on the other side of which ran a pebble-covered dirt road. I knew how those burning stones scorched the soles of bare feet. I lost sight of my sister then, but every single thing that happened to her that day she told me over and over.

Crossing a stretch of sandspurs, she started hopping again

4

to save her legs from the sharp stickers. She lost balance and fell smack into a patch of nettles. She got up, pulled off the nettles that had stuck to her, and hopped until she came to the drainage ditch, where she sat down on a clump of dry earth to slosh her tortured feet in the water. It was green and slimy—it always was—and in it floated refuse and rusty tin cans. But the wetness soothed her a little.

She had been crying, and when she wiped away the tears with the backs of her hands, she left streaks of mud across her forehead and around her eyes and mouth. She waded across the ditch, scuffled up the muddy bank on the other side, and scampered off up the hard dirt path toward town. When she came to the first sidewalk, she stopped running.

It was so hot that Mingie skimmed it, first on heel and then on toe, until she reached the section where the royal palms swayed their branches between the cement and the sun. Now, as she went along, Mingie peered around the houses to spy someone whom she might ask for work. She spotted a likely house—a big, wide white one with green and white metal furniture on a porch which had no roof but was covered with leafy vines. It was a pretty place, and Mingie was sure the people who lived there must be real rich and would need somebody to keep leaves swept away from that beautiful porch.

It took courage to approach that house. Mingie always had courage, yet she tiptoed warily to the steps. Through the glass in the door she saw draperies move. The door swung open and a small girl in a yellow-flowered sunsuit looked out. "Mother!" she screamed. "There's a little nigger in our yard!"

A blond-haired woman hurried to the child and stormed at Mingie: "You better get! And don't you ever come back here again!"

Mingie fled across the street, her half sash whipping between her knees, her heart thumping. She ran to another block. On a vacant lot between two houses she tumbled to the cool grass beneath a huge magnolia tree and sat propped up by her hands. She felt light and hungry. It was past ten o'clock. Her breakfast had been a chunk of cold corn bread and syrup, and she had not had much more than that to eat all the day before.

Two small boys on bicycles appeared, saw her, and steered in her direction. She jumped up and stood trembling, her eyes questioning one boy and then the other.

"Nigger! Nigger!" the bigger boy shouted. The other banged his front wheel against Mingie's shins. She grabbed the handlebars and fought against it. "Take your black hands off my bike, you dirty nigger!" She bolted across the street almost in the path of a passing car. She ran until she could run no more and stood gasping for breath. She was near a big white two-story house with a low picket fence. An elderly woman in a light summer dress and thin apron was raking up scattered bits of palm leaves on the lawn. She was working backward toward the gate.

Mingie drew near and waited until the woman came close.

"Lady?" Mingie said, as politely as she knew how.

She startled the woman, who looked about and straightened as she saw a mop of black hair above the fence and two wide brown eyes staring between the pickets.

Mingie was winding her fingers in a fold of her flimsy skirt, wondering if should she run.

"What do you want, little girl?"

"Lady, do—do you want me to work fo' you?"

"You work for me?" the lady said.

"Yessum. I can rake yo' yard, an' I can clean them leafs off yo' porch an' sweep yo' sidewalk, an'—"

The woman smiled, and hers was a kind smile. But she

6

said, "Well, you're too small to be out looking for a job, and I've nothing you can do."

"Yessum," Mingie said and stuck her toes between the pickets. She climbed up until she could look over the fence. "Yessum, but I can wash the dishes an' scrub the kitchen— an' nurse yo' baby," she added hopefully.

"You'd better run on back home," said the woman. "There's nothing I want you to do, and I haven't a baby for you to nurse."

"You ain't got no baby?"

"No."

"Lemme finish up rakin' fo' you."

The woman said, "Now listen, little girl, you go on home."

"Yessum," said Mingie.

The woman went on raking, but soon she looked again at Mingie. "I said run on home."

"Yessum." Mingie got down from the fence while the woman watched her.

"Yessum." One must obey, but Mingie just stood there. She could not move. Here on the other side of the fence was kindness. It offered nothing; it told one to go away. It is easy enough to run from terrors. Heart and legs are made for it; they leap together. But to turn one's back on kindness—that is hard—too hard.

"Come here a minute, little girl," said the woman. "You're awfully small, but my granddaughter may find something for you to do."

"Yessum."

"Come here." She pushed the gate open and Mingie shot in, hitting the gate so hard that it banged against the pickets.

"Close it."

"Yessum," Mingie said, and did it. She followed the lady up the walk.

"Sit here while I call my granddaughter."

"Yessum." Mingie sat on the bottom step, which was shaded by a palm tree. She could hear the lady talking on the telephone.

"Is Rossie there? Yes. Hello, Rossie. There's a little old colored girl up here, Rossie, looking for work. Can you come over and talk to her? Oh, I don't know. Well, she looks to be 'bout seven or eight, I guess. I can't tell. But, Rossie—Yes, I know. She's hard to shoo away. No, I don't have anything for her to do—Rossie, I don't have time to fool with her. I wish you would—All right then. All right. Good-by."

Sitting there in the shade, Mingie felt cool and comfortable. The sweat was drying, leaving her skin shiny, except where the muddy streaks caked on her face. Her matted hair, crookedly parted down the middle, was tied in a knot on one side and bushed out on the other. Her feet and legs were scratched. Her dress—had it ever been new or clean? She did not know how she looked, had never thought about it. She just sat on the step, feeling quiet inside, not hoping, not thinking. Waiting.

A clean blue sedan rolled up. A woman stepped out and turned and lifted a chubby baby to her shoulder. She moved the gate open with one foot and closed it behind her in the same manner.

Mingie thought that she had never seen such a pretty woman.

She was tall and graceful in a light flowered summer dress and white sandals. She had a gentle mouth and smiling gray eyes, and her honey-brown hair was cut in long straight bangs. When her lips parted in a smile, as now, you saw beautiful, even white teeth; and her round cheeks rose slightly, sending tiny lines from the corners of her eyes. She walked in jaunty

8

little bounces, her shoulders swaying slightly. There was a gay air to her.

At the steps, she set the baby down and turned her to face Mingie. The baby, dressed only in a three-cornered diaper, flapped her chubby arms like two little pink wings.

"Hello, little girl," she said to Mingie. "Are you the one looking for a job?"

"Yessum."

For a moment the beautiful young woman stood silent, looking down at the black ragamuffin. It was a terribly important moment for Mingie, but she could do nothing but stare.

Then the woman smiled again. "My name is Mrs. Lee and this is my little girl, Edna, but we call her Edie. What is your name?"

"Min—Mingie."

"That's a pretty name. How old are you, Mingie?"

"Um eight—I think."

"Well, honey, I'm afraid you're not old enough or big enough for me to hire you—"

Mingie broke in by listing things she might do, as she had to Mrs. Lee's grandmother. "An' I think um nine—I think," she ended.

"Mingie, have you ever worked for anyone else before?"

"Yessum—yessum, I work for somebody."

"Whom did you work for?"

"I work for—I mean, I—"

Mrs. Lee did not press the point and shame Mingie.

"But you'll have to start school again soon, honey," she said.

"Noam, I ain't goin' to school when it open."

"Don't you go to school?"

"Noam—but I been a li'l bit. But don' go now."

"You don't? Well, does your mother know you're out looking for a job?"

"Noam. I ain't got no mother. She died when I was one minute ol'—or two minute ol'—I think."

"Didn't you ever have any mother to live with?"

"Yessum. I had a stepmama one time, but she done went an' took everything outa the house an' runned 'way. An' she ain't comin' back no mo'. I guess she don' like me an' Veanie."

"Maybe it isn't that she doesn't like you, dear—"

"But she beat me an' Veanie."

"Who is Veanie?"

"She my sister. She home."

"Who else lives with you, besides your sister?"

"My papa. But he sick, he can' walk."

"Oh, I'm awfully sorry your papa is sick, Mingie—"

"Yessum."

"How much do you want for working for me?"

"Oh—'bout fifty cent a week, I 'spect."

Mrs. Lee sat down on the step above, and that gave the baby's busy fingers a chance to grip Mingie's hair.

"Now, Edie, that's not a good girl, darling. You mustn't," Mrs. Lee said as she restrained the tugging little hand. She patted Mingie on the shoulder.

"It didn' hurt." The little warm hand had felt good in her hair.

"What will you do with the money you make, Mingie?"

"Um gonna buy me and Veanie some shiny black slippers and rose-color socks."

"What kind have you now?"

"I ain't got none now. Veanie ain't neither. My mama bought Ceal some but she didn' buy us none 'fore she went."

"Who is Ceal?"

"She my stepsister, but she gone with her mama now."

Countless times through the years we've wondered, my twin sister and I, what our lives would have been if, as Mrs. Lee looked down at Mingie, she had made a different decision.

"Well, you come along with me. We'll go over to my house," she said. Rising, she called back through the door, "Grandma, I'm taking the little girl over home with me."

Mingie trailed Mrs. Lee to the car and climbed into the front seat.

"Look, honey. Suppose you sit behind all big by yourself and let the baby sit here by me."

"I could hol' her."

"I think she'd better stay with me."

Mingie scrambled out. "How ol' is your baby?"

"She's five months old."

"I wish I could hol' her. I love babies."

"You can later. She's sleeply now. She hasn't had her nap."

"Yessum."

Mingie sat, all big by herself, on the rear seat; she had dreamt of nothing like this when, only a short time ago, she had been an outcast. She did not try to peer into the future nor look back to what had been. The shining wonder of this moment was complete in itself.

Mrs. Lee drove three blocks, slowed in the middle of the fourth, turned into a shell-strewn driveway, and stopped beside a fine house near a huge mango tree that was heavy with big red and yellow fruit.

"This your house?"

"Yes, it's mine, honey. You like it?"

"Yeah, ma'am. I like it."

Mrs. Lee carried Edie to the door. "Come on in, Mingie." she invited and unnecessarily cautioned, "Be careful the shells don't hurt your feet. They're hot."

In the living room Mrs. Lee set the baby down on a pink

blanket in the center of the blue and white floral rug. The room was more beautiful than Mingie had ever glimpsed, skimming through the hot streets or running for dear life; it was sweetly cool and smelled good. She moved about, inspecting, and her grimy hands reached out. Suddenly she was standing on the seat of a big soft armchair reaching for a picture on the wall.

"Honey," Mrs. Lee said quickly, "come and talk to Edie while I get her rubber doll. Then you can help me."

"Yessum." Mingie slid down leaving two smears of dirt on the upholstery. "Can I set down there an' nurse the baby?"

"Wait just a minute, Mingie. Listen. Wouldn't you like to get all cleaned up first so you'll be all fresh and cool?"

"Ye-yessum."

"Well, come with me. I have something I bet will fit you and I think you'll like it."

"Yessum. But can't I do nothin' for the baby?"

"Give her that ball."

"Yessum." Mingie rolled a big rubber ball to the baby, and Mrs. Lee fluffed pillows around her. "She'll be all right now. Come along." Mrs. Lee led Mingie across the hall to a bedroom where she opened a deep cedar chest.

"You help me look, honey."

Mingie was close at her side as Mrs. Lee searched in the chest and drew out a short blue dress. She held it up for a moment and then laid it across Mingie's outstretched arms. "Hold this a minute while I get the other part."

"Yessum. O-e-e-e! This pretty!"

Mingie and I will never forget that dainty dress with its puffed sleeves, full-gathered neckline, and white lace, and with its pink roses embroidered in the sleeve bands and the collar.

Mrs. Lee pulled out a pair of matching bloomers. "Here you are, honey."

12

Mingie snatched them from her. "O-e-e-e, they pretty! Can I put 'em on now?" She didn't wait for Mrs. Lee to answer. Her single garment—her old, too-long dress—fell in a tattered heap around her feet, and Mingie was scrambling to find her way into the new one.

How could Mrs. Lee have shown no shock or distaste as she saw the unwashed state of Mingie's body? She betrayed none.

"Mingie, wouldn't you like a nice hot bath? Then you'll be cool for your new things."

"Yessum."

"Then fold them neatly and bring them to the bathroom."

Mingie followed, hugging her precious new clothes. In the hallway, she waited while Mrs. Lee looked in on Edie.

"She's all right," Mrs. Lee said, and went on to the bathroom.

Mingie stopped at the door.

"Come on in, honey. Put your things there on the commode."

Mingie took a hesitant step, her eyes wide as they stared at the white porcelain and shining nickel and spotless mirror.

"Right here, honey."

"Yessum." Mingie put the clothes down and smoothed them out.

"That's right," Mrs. Lee said and ran the water into the bathtub.

"O-e-e-e! Um gonna git in the bathin' tub?"

Mrs. Lee felt the water. "Yes, but when you're all through, you have to take this powder and wash out the bathtub." She set a box of Dutch cleanser on the bath mat.

"Yessum."

"Now hop in."

Holding her breath with excitement, Mingie crawled in. Mrs. Lee handed her a bar of soap and emptied a cupful of Ivory Flakes around her. "This soap?" Mingie asked as she picked up handfuls of the snowy foam and smeared it over herself.

"Yes, it's soap. Didn't you ever see any like it?"

"Noam. But I seen some o' that big square white kind Mama make. She put potash in it an' cook it in a pot."

"My, I bet that's nice soap," Mrs. Lee said. "Here's a cloth. Rub yourself real hard so you'll be cool."

That was the way Mrs. Lee started speaking to us and it was the way she always spoke, instinctively choosing the right words. It would not have been the same if she had said: "So you'll be *clean*."

She left Mingie in the tub and went to her baby.

Mingie did not hurry her bath; it was too pleasant and too strange and puzzling an experience. She did not know quite what to do sitting in the gleaming tub in all that warm water. She rubbed herself, then sat smelling the scented bar of soap. Mrs. Lee returned. "Here's a towel, honey. When you're through don't forget to—"

The doorbell rang. Mrs. Lee paused, then crossed her lips with a finger. "Now don't make any noise," she said, and went out and closed the door.

Mingie sat still and listened. It was another woman who came in and talked with Mrs. Lee in the parlor. After a while Mingie heard: "Rossie, I've never seen your bathroom since you had it done in yellow and white."

Mrs. Lee said: "Well, Ethel, it's not quite finished yet."

The other woman said: "But I'd love to see what you're doing." And Mingie thought her voice was nearer.

"But honey, you wouldn't want to see it now. Wait until I

get my new curtains hung and the dressing table complete. I'd rather you'd wait, Ethel."

Mingie looked up at the fresh curtains hanging over her head and at the beautiful dressing table. She knew Mrs. Lee was putting off the other white lady and she knew why.

"All right then, Rossie," Mingie heard. "Well, it's time for lunch. Be sure to call me when your bathroom is finished."

"Yes, Ethel, I will. But come on over any time."

Mingie heard the front door close, and then Mrs. Lee talking to her baby. When she came into the bathroom, she said nothing about the caller. "Honey, have you had a nice bath?"

"Yessum."

"Stand up and let me see you."

Mingie scrambled to her feet. "Um through."

Mrs. Lee looked her over. "Wait. Let's turn on the light and have a good look."

Mingie's eyes followed Mrs. Lee's hand to the frosty yellow globe shade over the lighting fixture. "O-e-e-e, that pretty!"

"You like it?"

"Yessum."

"Listen, honey, you must wash your arms and all around your neck a little more. And rub real hard up near the edges of your hair."

"Yessum."

Mrs. Lee glanced at her watch, removed it, and laid it on a chair. "Sit back down, honey, and give me the cloth. Let me help you."

When the bath was over, Mrs. Lee said: "Pull out the stopper and wash the sides of the tub while the water is running out. I'm going to the kitchen to start lunch. When you've cleaned the tub real, real good with the powder, then get dressed."

"Yessum."

Mrs. Lee left her but soon returned. She sprinkled the mottled tub with the cleanser and showed Mingie how to scrub the porcelain. Then she helped Mingie reverse the blue dress which she had put on backward.

Mingie asked: "Now can I go in there an' nurse the baby?"

"Yes, honey, but don't try to lift her. Just let her play as long as she will, and hand her back the toys she keeps throwing out of reach. She might be sleepy, so if she starts to nod, call me." Mrs. Lee smiled down at Mingie. "You look cute, honey. I wore that little dress when I was about your size, only I was six."

Mingie hurried to the parlor where Edie, tired of playing, was fretting among the pillows on the floor. Mingie pulled her up to a sitting position and tried to amuse her. Soon there was a thud and a scream from Edie. Mrs. Lee rushed in from the kitchen to find Mingie astraddle the baby's back, holding her around the stomach so that only her hands and feet touched the blanket.

Mrs. Lee took possession of her child. Mingie backed away.

"Did you pick her up?"

"No, ma'am," Mingie denied, trembling.

Mrs. Lee carried Edie into the bedroom and closed the door.

Mingie stood there filled with remorse and fear. Everything in her told her to run, run, never stop running till she got home. But at home were Veanie and Papa, waiting, and nothing to eat. And Mrs. Lee hadn't said, "Get out!" She hadn't looked as if she was going to say it.

Mingie stood there on the blue and white rug. Run! Stay!

She heard Mrs. Lee coming from the bedroom. Run!

She took one step in flight, but looked back and saw Mrs. Lee's face. It was grave but not hard, contorted, not angry. For Mingie the room became all a blur. Tears ran down her cheeks.

"Mingie, did you take the baby up?" Mrs. Lee asked quietly.

"No—noam."

"Mingie, you must not tell an untruth; nobody likes little girls who tell lies. You did, didn't you?"

"No—yessum. She went to sleep an' I—"

"But I told you to call me. It's always best to tell the truth about it, Mingie."

"Y-yessum. Did I hurt yo' baby?"

"No, honey. She was just frightened a little. She's asleep now."

Mrs. Lee put a palm on Mingie's back and walked with her to the kitchen. "Get some potatoes and wash them." She pointed to the bottom cabinet drawer. "Take out five and put them in the sink. You can stand on this stool." And with a foot, she pushed a low red stool to the sink.

Mingie hauled out the biggest potatoes she could find. When Mrs. Lee noticed them, she said: "Why honey, I meant the white potatoes, not the sweet ones."

"This what kind I like," Mingie explained, hugging a heavy yam.

"Oh. Well, there's one already done in the oven and you can have it for your lunch. Now get out the others."

Mingie was busily and happily at work when there was a step on the porch. "I didn't know it was so late," Mrs. Lee said distractedly and hurried to the door to greet her husband.

"Hi, there, my honey!" Mingie heard, followed by a kiss. "Where's my best little gal friend?"

"Oh, she's asleep." Arm in arm, Mr. and Mrs. Lee came to the kitchen.

"Rossie, what was that I saw in there?" Mr. Lee asked. He had caught a glimpse of Mingie darting behind the stove.

"Come and see."

Mingie forced herself out of her inadequate hiding place. She stood winding her fingers in her new dress.

"Well, now, who have we here? Rossie, where did you find her?"

"Tell Mr. Lee who you are, honey," Mrs. Lee urged.

Mingie looked down at the floor.

"Cat's got her tongue," Mr. Lee teased.

"Her name's Mingie," Mrs. Lee helped.

"Mingie what? What's your last name, Mingie?"

Mingie's eyes rose for a moment to his bright blue eyes and his head of thick dark hair, then dropped to his glossy shoes. Then the shoes went away, and the slim white sandals, too.

Mingie listened.

"Oh, honey, I'd like to keep her for just a few days," Mrs. Lee pleaded.

"But Rossie, what can a little old girl like her do?"

"I know there's not much she can do, but can't we do something for her? She's begging for a job to make some money for a pair of shoes for herself and her sister."

"She's not much more than a baby. She ought to be home. Where's her mother?"

"She said she doesn't have a mother."

"Who are her people?"

"I don't clearly know yet."

"Surely you don't intend to let her fool around with the baby, honey. You'd better find out who she is and—"

From the kitchen Mingie called loudly, "My name Mingie Bennett."

"Well, I do believe she can talk after all," Mr. Lee said. With Mrs. Lee, he came back to the kitchen where Mingie stood silent as before, fingering her dress. "Now she's going to tell us all about herself," said Mr. Lee. But Mingie could not, and Mrs. Lee helped her by saying to her husband, "Go on, honey, and get ready for lunch."

When he left the kitchen, Mrs. Lee patted Mingie's shoulder. "You set up Edie's little table here for yourself, Mingie, and I'll put your plate on it."

"Yessum. Can I have my 'tater?"

Mingie could hardly wait, watching Mrs. Lee pile the blue dinner plate full.

From where he sat at his lunch, Mr. Lee could see Mingie's head above the low partition that separated the breakfast nook from the kitchen. Soon he noticed her lapping her plate like a starved puppy.

"Give her something else to eat," he said.

"Mingie dear, do you want something more?" Mrs. Lee asked. "Did you eat your potato?"

"Yessum."

"We're through now, Mingie," Mrs. Lee said a few minutes later. "You can come to our table now and eat as much as you want." And, as Mingie came, Mrs. Lee glanced down at the shining plate now holding only the rough stem of the huge potato.

Mr. Lee was going back to his office and his wife went to the front porch with him. When she returned to the dining nook, the empty dishes surprised her. She looked at Mingie, seated at the table with her chest held closely against it. Mingie was stuffing herself so that her thin cheeks puffed out. Only two rolls remained. They were in Mingie's fists. Four other rolls had disappeared, a large portion of steak, a half bowl of string beans, potatoes, and fresh tomato salad. Mrs. Lee's face paled. "Honey," she said, "haven't you eaten enough now? You might get sick. Come on. Let's put the rest of your bread away. You can eat it later."

Mingie crowded half a roll into her mouth and went on chewing. Mrs. Lee saw that her dress was bulging oddly. "What on earth do you have in there?" she asked. Then she noticed greasy and tomato-colored stains and realized where much of the food had been stowed away. "Mingie, what have you been doing? You've ruined your new dress!"

Tears rolled down Mingie's cheeks. She gulped, swallowing.

"Why did you do this, Mingie?"

"I—I—" Mingie tried to speak.

"Go on. Tell me."

"I was—was gonna carry Veanie some."

"That's not the right way to get things for your sister, Mingie. I'd have given you that food for her, if you'd told me you wanted to take her some. Now nobody likes people who take things on the sly. It's really stealing. Don't you ever do that again. Do you understand?"

"Ye-yessum."

"Now take all of that stuff out and put it on a plate and look in the cabinet drawer and bring me some paper sacks."

"Yessum."

Soon three small sacks were filled and put in a large one; the dress had been cleaned as well as it could be and had been hung out on the back porch to dry. Mrs. Lee washed and Mingie dried the dishes. "Don't you think you'd better go home now?" Mrs. Lee said. "Your papa and sister must be wondering about you."

"Is um comin' back tomorrow?"

It seemed to Mingie that Mrs. Lee hesitated a moment, and the world, suddenly bright and new, grew dim. Then she said, "Yes, you can come back tomorrow. Now run out on the porch and get your dress."

The ripe mangoes on low limbs hung near the porch. "Kin

I have some o' them mangoes to carry to Veanie?" Mingie begged.

"Why of course, honey. Get another bag out of the drawer and go out and pick some. Don't worry about how you'll carry them. I'll leave Edie at my mother's and then I'll drive you home."

2

THE CABIN was of unpainted boards so warped that most of them stood out from their nails. The roof bulged here and sagged there and, like the rest of the shack, kept out the glare. But it was useless against the heat of the Florida sun. Often it was hotter inside than out. There was no shade, for there were no trees. A forlorn feather of green dog fennel beside the rickety porch was the sole bit of shrubbery. Everywhere were weeds and rusty cans, rubbish and broken bottles. An elbow of pitted stovepipe stuck out through a jagged hole and was held in place by rusty wires.

The day had been more worrisome than usual for me, alone with Papa. He was no sicker; I knew he wasn't sick at all in the sense of having a fever that might kill him. He hadn't a fever. He was bedridden and helpless, but nobody said he was sick to death.

I knew about death and some of the ways in which it came. But that day I wasn't worrying about Papa dying, but about—everything. Mingie had been gone so long.

22

She'd said she would get a job and make some money. But could she? She could get into a pile of trouble, and then where would I be? And Papa had to have both of us to take care of him, even to turn him over.

When a shiny new car appeared and kept on coming toward the shack, I was seized with fear. A car in our wasteland where no car ever came, what could it mean but trouble? Something terrible had happened, was about to happen. The car stopped. Yes, whatever bad thing it brought was meant for us. Shaking, I kept out of sight and watched.

Mingie jumped out of the car, a different Mingie. She had on a beautiful dress and hugged a big paper sack, and her face shone as new as her dress. A strange white woman in a light blue frock got out. She, too, carried a paper sack. She came with Mingie to the cabin.

Mingie put her big sack on the edge of the splintery porch boards. "You gotta crawl up," she warned the white woman. "You can' walk on them steps. They done broke down."

Anyone could see it. "All right, honey," the woman said. She tried a post before pulling herself up by it. Mingie was calling to me: "Veanie, come an' look what I got for you! Veanie!"

I didn't move and I didn't answer. Mingie and I looked exactly alike; nobody could tell us apart, just seeing us. But we weren't the same inside us.

"Isn't your sister here, Mingie?" the woman asked.

"Yessum. She got to be. Papa, he never can do nothin' for hisself. Veanie's here."

Still frightened, I showed myself in the door.

"There she is," the white woman said in her pleasant voice. "Come on out, Veanie. I want to see you."

Mingie said, "Veanie, you got somethin' good to eat— 'taters an' meat, an' beans an' 'maters, an' biscuits an' stuff.

An' we got a whole lot a mangoes Mrs. Lee here give us, too."

I stayed inside the door and I didnt speak, so my sister explained me. "She kinda shame, Veanie is. Come on an' git eatens, Veanie. See, I got on a new dress Mrs. Lee give me— an' bloomers with trimmin' on 'em."

I darted out, snatched up the nearer sack, and ran back into the cabin. I tore open the sack and began eating. Mrs. Lee stayed on the porch and kept Mingie with her. I heard them talking.

"Why, Veanie looks just like you. You didn't tell me; are you twins?"

"Yessum, we twins. She eight, too—or nine, too, I think—"

"Yes," Mrs. Lee laughed delightedly. "Well, you're surely cute. Can't you get her to come out here? I want to see you together."

"Noam, not now. But she might come out when you done been here a long time. She shame. She don' like to talk to nobody strange at first."

I ate on, stuffing myself from the sack and staring out at the strange white woman who appeared to be owned by my sister. Mrs. Lee was silent as she glanced about. At last she asked, "Your father's in there, Mingie?"

"Yessum. He can't be nowhere else. He can' move."

Again Mrs. Lee looked about and I knew right off it was to gather courage for her next step.

"May I go in, Mingie?"

"Yessum. You kin go in."

Forever, I see my home as it was when Mrs. Lee first visited it. A recent hurricane had peeled back sheets of rusty tin from the roof, and they had not been nailed down again; the burning rays of the summer sun streamed in. Termites had lived here longer than we had, and their work showed in the eaten walls of the shack. Two high shutters hung lopsided at the paneless windows over which newspaper had been pasted; the paper was yellowed and torn. In every corner there were mouse holes, and now that there was food again the mice were boldly running about.

I retreated with my sack to the back room where, from behind the door, I watched Mrs. Lee enter the cabin. She flinched but did not draw back.

She caught sight of me. "Come here, Veanie."

I didn't answer, and again Mingie explained me: "Veanie ain' ready to talk yet."

"All right, honey, we won't bother her now. Where is your papa?"

"He in there—where Veanie is."

Mrs. Lee hesitated. She glanced at the stained paper that served for a pane in one of the windows. I still remember what it said, "House Beautiful," in black letters. She looked at the unpainted table beneath it, one of its legs a makeshift of splintery two-by-four timber. On top, in the dust, rested a small glass kerosene lamp with a broken smoke-streaked shade. She saw the sway-bellied cot leaning along the back wall and the seatless chair with a wooden box answering for the fourth leg.

She turned her eyes to the door behind which I was hiding. "Is your papa asleep, Mingie?"

"Noam, he ain't sleep. But he can' talk."

Mrs. Lee took her hand and Mingie led her through the doorway. She had to pause to get used to the darkness of the room and also—as I, even on that day, realized—to adjust herself to the heavy, sour smell.

"Where is he, honey?"

"He right over there."

Then Mrs. Lee heard the coarse, raspy mumble of a paralyzed man attempting to speak.

Mrs. Lee asked: "Mingie, can you open the window so some light can come in?"

Mingie looked up at the brown burlap nailed over Papa's window. "Yessum, I reckin."

"Pull it down," Mrs. Lee urged. "I'll help you put it up again."

"Yessum." Mingie tore the burlap from its rusty nails and the hot sun streamed in.

Mrs. Lee walked to the cot that sagged even deeper than the one in the other room. Papa lay, as always, on his back. His bony frame showed under a thin, tattered blanket.

"Hello!" she said, trying to force brightness into her tone.

Papa could only mumble as he dragged his better hand tremblingly from the edge of the cot and tried to reach out toward his visitor.

"It's all right," Mrs. Lee said. She took Papa's wasted brown hand in one of hers and placed the other gently over it. Papa's fingernails, long and clawlike, curled in her fresh white palm; Papa's knuckles were stiff and knotty. He mumbled again, baring his yellow, stained teeth between his distorted lips that pulled upwards toward his half-closed left eye. His right eye stared, wide and wretched, beneath his black brow and his head of mixed-gray, linty hair.

"It's all right," Mrs. Lee repeated. "Don't try to talk. I think I understand."

At her side, Mingie reminded her, "He can' talk none."

But Papa struggled to be understood. He tried for voice by opening his mouth wider, but from it came only a cough heavy with the odor of unswallowed food. He realized it was no use, and tears wet the creases of his wrinkled cheeks.

Mrs. Lee had to close her eyes, and when she opened them, I saw that they were wet.

I found myself standing beside her. She took her hand

from Papa's and touched my shoulder. "Veanie, honey, I'm glad you came to see me."

I didn't answer for a minute. Then I said, "It got maggits in Papa's bed."

Mrs. Lee gasped. I cried and began wiping my tears with my skirt.

Mrs. Lee's white fingers reached into a pocket and drew out a dainty blue handkerchief. As she spread it, I saw pink roses and the letters "R. L." in white. I reached for it, but Mingie said, "You ain' sposes to touch nobody's things 'less they tell you to or you ast 'em—huh, Mis'—Mis' Rossie?"

"Yes, honey, but this is all right."

"It's pretty," I said.

"Mis' Rossie give me this pretty dress, Veanie," my sister said, "an' look—bloomers, too. An' they got trimmin' on 'em." She showed me.

"Do you like this handkerchief, Veanie?" Mrs. Lee asked.

"Ye-yessum."

"Well, you may have it."

"Say thank you, ma'am, Veanie," said my sister.

"Thank ya, ma'am, Mis'—Mis'—"

"Mis' Rossie. Her name Mis' Rossie."

"Mis' Rossie," I ended and took the sheer bit of blue. Not even on Miss Rossie's command would I have used and soiled my treasure. I went to the corner and bumped to my knees before our broken-down bureau. It had only one drawer, at the bottom, and when I pulled it open a loose panel tumbled out. I smoothed down the clothing kept there and carefully laid the handkerchief on top. I closed the drawer and fitted back the board in place.

Miss Rossie had watched me. Now she turned her eyes to our kitchen gear: the rusty, potbellied stove which stood on three of its own legs and a stack of old red bricks for a fourth;

the homemade table covered with newspaper; the chipped and cracked dishes; two battered boxes and a screenless safe swarming with flies and cockroaches. The back room, Papa's room, served also as our kitchen.

"Mingie, honey, do Veanie and you have money for food?"

"Noam, we ain't got none now, but that lady down there"—my sister pointed in the direction of Aunt Tiller's house—"she give us two dimes sometime an' we buy some meal and syrup, an' the Sunday school people give us some groc'ry—"

"An' we go to the packin' house an' git some grapefruit an' oranges," I cut in. "I cook corn bread," I added proudly. I was no longer in the least afraid of Miss Rossie, and I was less afraid of other things, too. After that very first meeting with her, I wasn't so afraid.

"Do you give that to your papa?" Miss Rossie asked me.

"Yessum. But he can't eat so good."

"Does he have anything else?"

"Yessum. Sometime that lady bring him some soup an' he eat some of it."

Miss Rossie stepped to the back door and stared out at a wilderness of weed and brush spotted here and there with a bright stalk of wild-growing four-o'clock. After a moment she turned and looked down at us. "Well, I'm going now," she said, "but I'll be back with some food."

"For Papa too?" Mingie asked.

"Yes. He's going to have some nice hot soup."

She came back, as she promised. That night, I felt different. For the first time in my life I went to sleep feeling that something good might be waiting for me when I woke up.

3

AS MINGIE HAD TOLD Mrs. Lee, our mother had died when we were born. The mama we had known was a huge dark woman with a huge dark voice. She was easily angered, quick to move when she got angry, and always ready with the switch.

Indelible in my memory is a cold, windy, late September afternoon in the year when Mingie and I were about six. We lived in a different place and in a bigger and better house then. Papa was a strong man and a good worker. He wasn't going to be home that day. He had gone to a special job in a nearby city.

My stepmother and her daughter, who was larger and older than Mingie and me, were going about pulling down curtains and packing them with other things. I didn't know why, nor did Mingie, and it was safer not to ask.

Mingie and I were playing on the kitchen floor near the stove when Mama came to the door. Her narrow eyes were flashing and her short hair was standing up all over her head. "Get up offa th' floor," she ordered. "Go down to the store an' get me some tomatoes." She paused. "An' stay down there till I get there."

Fearful of her, I jumped to my feet. Mingie picked up the twenty-five-cent piece that Mama tossed to her. "Is Ceal goin' too?" she asked.

"No. Now get out an' go on!" She took a step toward us.

We left running and never stopped until we were far down the railroad tracks.

Often I had wanted to run away from home but Mingie always argued with me to wait until we were bigger and knew some place to go. "Mingie?" I said, opening the old argument.

"Huh?"

"Mingie, le's run away now an' don' never come back no mo'."

"No, Veanie. We ain' got nowhere to go."

"Well, don' cha wish Papa take us with him when he go to work?"

"Yeah. Ol' Mama git meaner when he ain' here."

"Yeah. I hate 'er. I hate 'er real bad. I wish she die."

"No, Veanie. Don' say ya hate 'er. Papa say for us not to hate nobody."

"Yeah. An' he won' even let us tell 'im how mean she is no time."

"He say she jus' want us to be good, an' things gonna git better. But nothin's better. He know she mean, all right. Come on."

By the time we reached the general market, dark heavy clouds were heaping up in the sky. A storm was about to break and we were afraid of storms. As soon as we got the tomatoes I wanted to go home, but Mingie reminded me that we had to wait for Mama to come for us.

We waited. Soon the store was closing and we had to go outside. Men hammered boards across the window and the wide green door; they climbed into a truck and drove away. Everyone was gone now. Just Mingie and I stayed there. It was getting darker every minute and rain started to come down. We were still dry under the shelter in front of the store, but the wind was blowing harder. It was blowing the rain in on us. "We can' stay here. Come on, le's go."

"No. We gotta wait some mo'," Mingie said. She was more afraid of Mama than of the storm and, for a while, thinking of Mama, I was too.

Finally we set out. The rain was cold. It beat through our thin dresses, plastering them to us, and then the wind would pull our skirts away. The paper sack was soaked. The tomatoes fell through and splashed on the ground. Mingie picked up even the broken tomatoes and heaped them in her skirt. "Oh, Veanie!" she sobbed as I helped her. "They all mashed up. Mama gonna beat me, I know."

"Yeah," was all I could say. But there was nothing to do but go on.

There was no light in our house and the front door was unfastened and blowing back and forth. Mingie opened the screen and stepped in. "Oh, oh, Veanie," she cried out, "ain' nothin' here. Mama an' Ceal mus' be done gone."

I was too frightened to believe it. "Um scared, Mingie. She might be in there—gone to bed—"

"No she ain', 'cause if she was, she be waitin' with her ol' green limb in her hand."

Mama always called her switches her green limbs. She would go out and carefully choose them and let them dry just long enough to get good and tough before she used them on us.

Mingie was right; Mama and Ceal were gone, and with them, Mama's possessions. That's what she alway called them, and I suppose most of them were hers. She had left us mighty little: a table, a lamp with no shade, a chair. In the bedroom was the old, sagging cot we had often played on; its black, dry moss mattress had burst and was bulging.

"What we gonna do, Mingie?" I asked.

"I—I don' know."

"I wish Papa would come."

"Yeah. Maybe he will now 'cause it's stormin' so he can' work on buildin' houses."

"Yeah." I felt a little better.

We lay down on the cot, wet as we were, and hugged together. Finally we fell asleep.

It was far past midnight when Mingie shook me and whispered: "Veanie, I hear somethin' out there."

"Maby it's Papa. Or ol' Mama," I whispered. We listened to the footsteps. Then a match flared up and went out. Peering through a crack in the wall, we saw Papa strike match after match and hunt about until he found the table. He lit the lamp and, holding it in one hand, he just stood there, his face blank as he looked about the empty room.

Mingie called, "Papa!" and after a little he came to our room. "Come on in, Papa," Mingie said, and when he pushed open the door, she jumped out of bed and threw her arms about his waist. "Papa, Mama done gone 'way. She gone an' she took all th' things, too."

I wondered what Papa was thinking as he stood there, saying never a word, hugging Mingie. I stood up on the cot and, still without speaking, he came and put his arm around me so tight it nearly hurt.

Papa wanted Mama back, and he went looking for her. After about a week he found her and got her to come back. Now it was worse for Mingie and me than it had been before.

Mama was angry all the time. We stayed away from her all we could. Papa never said so to us, but we knew it was worse for him, too.

One terrible morning, Papa couldn't get out of bed; he was paralyzed on one side—hand and foot—and he couldn't speak. Mama left us again. As before, she took with her most of the furnishings. Still Papa wanted her back. He couldn't go look for her himself but he made Mingie and me understand he wanted us to find her. We tried but couldn't; nobody ever did.

We had to move out of the house to a shack about a mile away that rented for fifty cents a week. A neighbor helped us, finding the new place and making the arrangements. I can never forget that moving, with Papa propped up on the seat of an old wagon, his useless arm (which used to be so strong) lying limp across Mingie's lap. He was so weak, and so shamed inside him, that he couldn't keep the tears from running down his cheeks. The neighbor who was helping us had to half-drag, half-carry Papa from the wagon into the shack and lay him down in that old, sagging cot in which—some two and a half years later—Mrs. Lee was to find him.

Then we were by ourselves, Papa and Mingie and me. We had to look after Papa and ourselves as best we could. We had to eat. Somehow we had to get food.

This was the way we took to do it.

We'd be up early, with the first light of day, and tiptoe out so as not to wake Papa. Each of us carried a crocus bag. When we neared our chosen field or truck garden, we would drop down and crawl, like commandos raiding enemy territory. After filling our bags with the best vegetables we could find at the edge of the field, we retreated as we had come. Sometimes we were seen and frightened off by angry shouts. Once a shot was fired. After helping ourselves from a field, we kept away from it for a while.

About a mile from our cabin we discovered a grove of wild mulberries and guavas. They were good trees, giving plenty of fruit, and nobody was watching them. When a raid on a garden or field seemed too risky, we'd go to the grove and gather the berries on the ground and we'd climb the low-limbed guava trees for their fruit. Not being afraid there, we would sit under the trees and eat—too much. We'd fill our stomachs only to have them ache; often we'd both be sick. We were safe from shouts and shots, but we didn't have for ourselves, nor were we bringing Papa, a satisfactory meal.

Once we ran down a rabbit in the palmettos and killed it with sticks. It hurt us to kill, but we couldn't afford to be squeamish. That cornered, quivering little animal was meat, and it was nourishing soup for Papa.

The day came when there was scarcely a handful of meal left in the tin can on the shelf, and nothing to cook it with.

We had been watching a little house not far from ours; it was visible from our porch. An old woman almost crippled by rheumatism lived there alone. On some days, we noticed, she would hobble out and be gone for hours. We saw her leave the morning we found ourselves without meal or fuel.

"Veanie," said my sister, "we go over to that ol' woman's an' git some o' her stuff while she gone. Hear?"

I had no more scruples than she did, but I was more timid. "We might git caught, Mingie. She might come back. Anyway the door be locked, sure."

"No, it ain'. I seen her when she went out, an' she jus' pull the door to."

"But um scared—"

"Well, I'll go. You stay on th' porch an' watch for me. An

34

if ya see her comin', holler real loud an' I'll go on pas' th' house."

I agreed, and Mingie hopped off the porch and trotted across the yard to the edge of the tall palmettos. There she got down on all fours and began to crawl, so that all I could see was the top of her bushy head or the fans of the palmettos move as she brushed them. After a while, I saw her jump up and dart to the house and run in. Suddenly she was out again and lost in the palmettos. When she came out, she peered around cautiously.

"Come on, Mingie," I called to her, "ain' nobody 'bout." And I saw, as she stood up, that the skirt of her dress was caught up in a bundle. She scurried through the hot sand and shot past me into our house. "Shet th' door quick, Veanie," she whispered. "I got us somethin', but le's don' let Papa know where we got it."

"No. Le's tell 'im she give it to us."

Mingie had brought back some large slices of bacon, several biscuits, and a gob of green peas. "We gonna have us a good dinner, ain' we, Veanie?" she exulted.

"Yeah, Mingie. O-o-e-e-e!" I could taste the pork in my mouth.

"Papa, too."

She divided everything equally, mine and hers on the edge of the bare table; then she ran in to feed Papa. But he tried to talk to us and wanted to refuse to eat it, and Mingie had to stuff the mashed peas into his mouth and wash them down with water, almost choking him. So we knew that Papa somehow guessed we had stolen the food. He cried, and Mingie petted him and told him, "Ya gotta eat, Papa, so ya won' die."

We saw that the old woman had her suspicions of us. When she returned home and was inside a short while, she came out on her porch and stood looking our way. But she did nothing. So Mingie and I took turns going to her house and stealing her food.

Then one day we found her at our steps. We had not seen her coming. We were caught. Mingie stood her ground, and I peered out from behind her. The old woman leaned on a stick which might become a weapon, but she was not agile, and we were. She looked stern but not mean. She nodded at us and gave us "Good evenin' " like a real visitor. She told us her name was Tiller. All the white people she washed for, she said, called her Aunt Tiller, and we could call her that too.

Then, looking us dead in the eyes, she said: "Chil'en I don' never like fo' nobody to take nothin' from me. If I got anythin' ya want, as' me fo' it, an' if I got it to spare I'll give it to y'all." She started away, but turned on her cane. "Where ya mama?"

"She dead," Mingie said.

"Then who stay here with ya?"

"Papa," I answered and Mingie explained, "He sick. He can' walk."

"Can I see 'im?"

"Yessum. Ya can come in."

Aunt Tiller climbed the broken steps and went into Papa's room.

After that, we went over and asked Aunt Tiller for food. But sometimes we "borrowed" it when she wasn't there. Often there was little for us to "borrow." Aunt Tiller received only fifty cents a bundle for the clothes brought to her to wash, and when she went out to work by the day—on the days her "misery" permitted it—she earned a dollar. Yet sometimes she handed out a dime to each of us, to reward us for running errands.

36

She was a good old woman and very religious and sometimes she talked one of us into going to a "meeting" with her.

So for a while we stopped raiding gardens and fields. Instead we roamed after the avocados, guavas, and sappodillos that grew wild in some sections. And we took turns walking the three miles to the town-dock packing house for the cull oranges and grapefruit given away free. And we baited fish-hooks with corn to catch pigeons and wandering chickens.

Still we were hungry, and Papa's bones showed through his skin.

There was a boy who passed near our cabin on the sand road on his way to school; we had often seen him, swinging in one hand a tin bucket—of food, we were sure. He was much larger and stronger than we were, but there were two of us, and we planned a surprise.

Early one morning we hid in the tall, thick bushes that grew on both sides of the road. As he came around the curve carrying his books and his bucket, Mingie sprang out and knocked his legs from under him. He fell, scattering his books, and I snatched his pail and ran while Mingie pawed up handfuls of sand and dashed it into his eyes. Before he could clear his eyes and come after us, we were far away in the palmettos. We ate well that day. The bucket contained two large baked sweet potatoes, rice, corn bread, and two long strips of pork chitterlings.

Word of our misdeed reached Aunt Tiller, and she warned us: "Y'all chil'en gotta stop this stealin'. Tain' good. Ya gonna get in trouble sure's ya born. An' "—she raised her crooked oak stick and shook it at us, and had to set it back on the floor quick to support herself—"ya'll goin' to hell with ya eyes open, if ya don't mend yo ways." Her voice was serious and trembling, her hands shook on the stick, and she launched on a vivid and horrible description of hell.

"You know, Mingie, I don' never wanta die," I said to my sister when we were alone, " 'cause I sure don' wanta go to hell an' burn in all that fire."

"Me, neither. O-o-e-e-e; it sounds real, real hot."

On the next Sunday, Aunt Tiller was up early, hopeful that Mingie or I would board the wagon and go to church with her. The little house where they held services once a month was a mile down the road, and it was a good-neighbor gesture for one who had a horse and wagon to come by and pick up churchgoers who were less fortunate. Aunt Tiller never missed; she was always ready and waiting beside the lone road, no matter how badly she was ailing.

Aunt Tiller, in a long black outfit and black Sunday shawl, came hobbling through the sand on her oak stick.

"Mingie!" she called.

Mingie ran to the door; I stayed behind it, peering through the crack. "Ma'am?" Mingie answered.

"Which one o' y'all goin' with me this mornin'?"

"I can' go, Aunt Tiller, 'cause my shoes got the toe out—"

"That ain' nothin'. Go barefoot. Where Veanie? Ain't she goin'?"

I whispered through the crack: "Tell 'er mine done bust, too."

Mingie did it.

"Gal, y'all lyin'," said Aunt Tiller. "Jus' don' wanta go. But ya better get right. God ain' please at ya."

Aunt Tiller returned late in the afternoon. She came into our shack a bit more nimbly than usual. One fist was balled tight; her face was excited and beaming. "Mingie, come help me a little," she said. "Um tired."

Mingie hung on to Aunt Tiller until she eased herself in the old rocking chair.

"Good meetin' today. Look, Mingie—Veanie. Got somethin' fo' y'all."

Her trembling fingers tugged at a knot in the dingy handkerchief she had on her lap. She gave up and handed it to Mingie. "Here, you loose it."

When Mingie worked the knot loose, a small wad tumbled to the floor. Mingie snatched it up and put it in Aunt Tiller's outstretched palm. She fumbled out three dollar bills and flattened them on her knee.

"Brung y'all some money," Aunt Tiller said proudly. "Tol' the church 'bout y'all an' ya pa, an' they took up this fo' ya."

"O-o-e-e-e-! All this?"

"Yeah. Now, I ain' gonna give all o' it one time. Too much money."

"Yessum."

"Run in there, Mingie; tell ya pa y'all got a lotsa money the church done give ya."

"Yessum." Mingie happily skipped to Papa's room and skipped back.

"Now, like I said," Aunt Tiller proceeded, "I'm gonna give y'all jus' fifty cents. The other um gonna keep an' let y'all get it as ya need it. Now I don' want y'all goin' out stealin' no mo'. Lemme see now. Want y'all to go buy ya se'f some grits, syrup, bacon, meal an' flour. Get a dime worth o' each one. Go in there, Veanie, an' bring me piece o' paper an' pencil."

I ran into Papa's room and returned with a piece of a paper bag. "Aunt Tiller, here some paper, but we ain' got no pencil."

"I got somethin' can write, Aunt Tiller," Mingie said and produced a gray, graphitelike rock she'd found on the railroad track. With it, Aunt Tiller scrawled on the bit of brown paper: "gris, bakin, mel, sirp, flor."

39

"Here now, gal, y'all run fas' as ya can 'fore the store close. I'll stay with ya pa till y'all get back."

Mingie tied the dollar in a rag and balled it in her fist.

The little store, run by a white farmer, was nearly a mile down the road. It kept open on Saturdays and Sundays until about eight o'clock to accommodate customers around the farmland who worked all week and got to the store only on those days.

The sun had already set and we ran nearly all the way. The store was still open. The storekeeper was sitting behind the counter reading a magazine under a hanging kerosene lamp.

"Mister, we want some groc'ry, please, s'r," Mingie said.

The man kept on reading. Mingie stepped around the counter, with me behind her. "Mister," she began again.

"Get out there, you niggers, and wait. You got no business back here."

We scurried around to the front of the tall counter where the man let us wait. At last he got up and eyed us.

"We—we wanta get some groc'ry," Mingie said, thrusting the crumpled brown paper across the counter. "Gimme these things on here. They wrote down. Th' money in here." She laid the dirty rag beside the paper.

"Not going to put my hands on that! Take the money out of there," the man ordered. "And tell me what you want."

"Yess'r." Mingie untied the knot and shook the bill out upon the counter. "We want a dime worth o' grits an' meal an' flour an' syrup an' bacon. An' I want fifty cent back."

From a box the storekeeper dug out some salt pork scraps and piled them in a newspaper. The other items he scooped out of barrels and weighed on the swinging scales. He rolled a fifty-cent piece across to Mingie and, leaving the dollar bill lying on the counter, went back to his chair and took up his magazine again.

While Mingie and I were gathering our purchases, I kept my eyes on the dollar bill. Suddenly I snatched it and pushed out the door ahead of Mingie and ran on down the road. She ran after me but I didn't let her catch up with me until we were a good distance from the store, when I told her: "Come on quick. I got back the dollar."

"O-o-e-e-e, Veanie! He done gimme the ha'f dollar—an' ya done stol' the dollar back, too!" she jubilated.

That was how much Aunt Tiller's depictions of hell-fire actually influenced us. We were far more affected by other fears.

But for once Mingie was more timid than I. "Veanie, I bet that man gonna know ya stol' that money, an' when we go back he gonna put ya in jail."

"No he ain't, 'cause I ain' goin' back no mo'."

"What we gonna tell Aunt Tiller?"

"Girl, ya crazy? Think us gonna let 'er know?"

"Veanie, um real, real scared 'bout it. We gotta take it back."

I stared at her, assailed by doubts. "Mingie, ya don' want none o' the money?"

"No. 'Cause um scared. We might git in jail."

I was scared, too—scared to keep the money and scared of returning it. Neither of us had stolen money before, and it was somehow different from stealing food. We were scared of the storekeeper and just as scared of the hot fires in Aunt Tiller's hell. For a week I hid that money in a jar under the box that supported one side of the stove and I worried myself sick about it; and when we wanted to spend the second dollar that Aunt Tiller doled out to us, we had to walk three miles to town to another store.

At last we spent the stolen dollar on cookies, bananas, pickled pigs' feet, and other things we ate guiltily by ourselves. So that dollar was gone and, all too soon, so was the rest of the money. For our needs, we resorted again to raids on farms and gardens.

Such was our situation—physical and moral—on the day Mingie discovered Mrs. Lee.

4

IN THE MORNING we got Aunt Tiller to promise to look after Papa for a while. Mingie was taking me with her to Miss Rossie's. She wore her beautiful blue dress. It seemed strange for me, the old Veanie, to be walking along beside a new Mingie. And when we came to the house, Mingie opened the gate as if she'd been doing it all her life. My heart ached. It was as though I had lost her.

Although she had told me over and over again about Mrs. Lee's house, I was still unprepared for what I saw. The house stood in a garden far back from the street. The long walk up to the front steps was lined with royal palms, each circled by yellow and purple pansies. The bottom of the house was brown and the upstairs white, and bougainvillia blossomed on the porch. It was a house I might have dreamt up and it "belonged" to Mingie! I trembled as we stood at the door.

Inside, it was even more wonderful. The walls were pale gray, and rose-colored curtains hung at the windows. Soft, cool colors contrasted with the dark, polished floors. I saw my first upholstered chairs and settees, and the first bookcase, and the first piano, and a mysterious tall cabinet—a radio. And under my bare feet was the soft, tickly feeling of a deep-piled rug. But I heard Mrs. Lee's voice as from far away. I was miserable. Never, never would she let li'l old Veanie stay here!

She had not been expecting me that day, yet she acted pleased to see me. After she had left our shack the day before, she must have been very busy. I can no longer clearly remember my feelings when she laid out for both of us, Mingie and me, dresses she must have sewed the night before, and shoes and socks she must have bought for us on her way home from our cabin. She had us put them on. I knew that Mingie's were hers to keep, like yesterday's blue dress. But I could not believe that mine were truly mine; I was sure I would have to give them back.

Mingie had told me that Mr. Lee came home to lunch. I dreaded his coming and tried to hide when I heard him on the steps, but Mingie wouldn't let me.

"Rossie!" he exclaimed as he saw me. "What's this now? Are you running a day nursery?"

"Oh, honey," said Mrs. Lee, "I just couldn't send them away!"

Mr. Lee stood looking at Mingie and me. As I stared up fearfully at him, a faint but unmistakably friendly smile melted his make-believe sternness. He glanced from one of us to the other, and the smile broadened. Then he shook his head, that smile still on his face, and went off to get ready for his lunch.

I looked at my sister and then down at myself. We were wearing pink and white gingham dresses, rose-colored socks, and shiny black slippers. They were exactly the same, in every detail. I was filled with a great and sudden joy, and we grinned at each other. Everything was fine. Mingie belonged to me again and I to her.

When Mr. Lee returned, we were setting Edie's big doll table for ourselves. "Which of you was here yesterday?" he asked.

Mrs. Lee turned me around. "This is—" she began, and corrected: "No, *that's* Mingie; she was the one. This is Veanie. She doesn't say much."

"Well, I don't believe either of these little old gals can talk," Mr. Lee teased.

Later, when he had gone and Edie was taking her nap, Mrs. Lee sat on the back porch with us while we shelled green peas. "Mingie," she said, "you and Veanie are going to school when it opens, aren't you?"

Mingie's eyes met mine. Finally she replied, "I don' know'm. 'Cause we got to stay with Papa."

Mrs. Lee turned to me. "Don't you think it would be nice if you could go to school, Veanie?"

"Ye-yessum."

"Then you'll have to be big girls and work together. One of you can go one day while the other stays home with your papa. Then the next day, the other can go. What about that, Veanie?"

I looked at Mingie for her to answer.

"How about it, Veanie?" Mrs. Lee asked patiently. "You want to read and write, don't you?"

Mingie explained for me: "Mis' Rossie, she scared the childum gonna laugh at her."

"Laugh at her for what, Mingie?"

"That's when we didn' have no shoes. They call us li'l dirty-foot Topsys."

"Yessum, an' I don' wanta go no more," I said.

"You have shoes now, and I have some others you can have. And some nice dresses. You'll look very pretty, so the children won't say those things about you any more."

"Yessum. Thank ya, ma'am," Mingie said right away, as she always could, and she urged me, "Say thank ya, ma'am, Veanie."

I gulped a thank-you but looked anxiously at Mingie. We wanted to work and earn money. More than anything else, we wanted to work right here for Miss Rossie.

As if reading my mind, Mrs. Lee went on: "And you can take turns helping me, too. Mingie, on your school days Veanie will be home looking after your father. Then when you come home Veanie will come here. And on Veanie's school days she'll go home and Mingie will come here. You see? In that way your father will always have one or the other of you to take care of him, and you'll both be working, and going to school. But you'll have to help each other with your lessons. Do you think you can do it?"

"Yessum," said Mingie promptly.

"Oh, yessum!" I cried.

"Meanwhile, until school opens, you can help me full time on alternate days. That means Mingie will come tomorrow, and you, Veanie, the day after, and then Mingie again, and so on. Would you like that?"

"Yessum!" This time we said it together.

The next morning, Mingie had a little trouble on the way to Mrs. Lee's house. As she approached it, two boys peppered her with handfuls of yellow coconut palm berries. They hurt. In a panic of fear, Mingie ran for the front porch. Mrs. Lee saw her and quickly unfastened the screen door and walked out on the porch saying, as she went past Mingie, "Go on in." Then she let the door swing to and she went to the stone pillar and gave the boys a go-away look. They shied off, and Mrs. Lee came into the house. "Mingie, honey," she said, "after this, come down that back street and to the back door so the children won't see you. If I'm not up, I'll leave the screen unfastened so you can sit on the porch and wait for me."

"Yessum."

"Now go to the kitchen and get your breakfast. I fixed you a plate."

So now Mingie knew—as much as a child can know—that Mrs. Lee could not change the world.

That day she broke a cup and two glasses while doing the dishes. As fast as she broke them, she put the pieces into a paper bag and stuffed it down into the garbage can. She cut her thumb on one of the pieces of glass.

Mrs. Lee saw drops of blood on the drainboard. "Did you cut yourself, Mingie?" she asked.

"Noam." Mingie was hiding her hands in the soapy water of the sink.

"What's this? It looks like blood."

"I don' noam."

"Let me see your hands, honey," Mrs. Lee said, and Mingie had to show her gashed thumb.

"There—you did cut yourself. Did you break something?"

"No-noam."

"You must have. Let's run the water out and see what cut you." Mrs. Lee removed the stopper, and when the water drained away, she examined the glasses and dishes only to find none chipped or broken, and there was no sharp knives.

"Where is it, Mingie?" Mrs. Lee asked, and waited.

Mingie was feeling miserable but she replied only: "Ma'am?"

"Whatever cut you. Where did you put it, Mingie?"

"In—in the bucket."

Mrs. Lee stood quietly looking at her for a moment before she said: "Were you afraid I'd be mad at you for breaking something?"

"Yessum."

"Well, Mingie, I told you the first day you came—remember?—that you must tell the truth no matter what you do. I'm not angry with you. I know you didn't mean to break anything. But if you want to come here, I want you to be truthful and honest above everything, at all times. Did you hear, Mingie? At all times."

If Mingie wanted to keep coming there! She and I had never wanted anything so much in all our lives. Heaven as a reward for right doing, and hell as a punishment for wrong, were remote and shadowy regions; not so that house of Mrs. Lee's.

"Ye-yessum," said Mingie. Her relief and her love for Mrs. Lee were so great that she could hardly speak.

Mrs. Lee led her to the bathroom where she put Mercurochrome and a bandage on the deep cut. "Um shame o' myself. I ain' gonna tell no mo' stories," Mingie pledged.

"I'm very happy that you aren't, honey."

" 'Cause I wanna come here."

"I want you to be truthful whether you're coming here or not."

To be honest with Mrs. Lee was one thing. But to be honest all the time, everywhere, in a world where we had learned too well the self-preserving tactics of evasion, that was something else again. To a child, any child, grownups can sometimes be remarkably impractical. However, a standard of behavior had been established, and Mingie and I accepted it.

48

On that same day, Mrs. Lee dealt in her way with the deep trouble that plagues colored children from the time they become aware of the disqualifications visited on them because of their skin.

Mingie had been playing with Edie, and now the baby lay among her pillows chuckling delightedly as Mingie tickled her palm. Mrs. Lee smiled down at them. "She's ready for her nap now."

Mingie looked at the little pink hand she held in her own. "I wish—I wish I was white, an' Veanie does too, so we could be your li'l girls," she said wistfully.

In her own words, Mingie brought to me Mrs. Lee's reply:

"We shouldn't wish to be what we are not, honey. God made us all the way He wanted us to be. He made us different colors and gave us different colors of eyes and hair, just as he made the birds and flowers different from each other in feathers and blossoms—for some good reason. He wanted white little girls and He wanted brown little girls too. White or dark, we can all make ourselves beautiful in His sight by being clean, decent, and loving.

"Honey, you said you liked my flower garden, didn't you?"

"Yessum. It pretty."

"Well, there are all kinds of flowers in it. That's the way the world is. The people are like flowers—all colors and kinds."

Mingie and I discussed that over and over. We had heard something like it said before, but not by anybody white.

The next day it was my turn to go. When Miss Rossie discovered me perched quietly on a stool on the back porch, she sleepily called, "Mingie, you can take the broom and go around front and brush the palm berries off the walk while I make breakfast."

"Yessum," I answered, without explaining who I was.

"Take that big paper box and put the berries in it. Don't try to carry it back; Mr. Lee will do that this evening."

"Yessum."

It was quiet and pleasant under the palm trees. It was safe; no wicked boys were about. I swept awhile, played marbles with the yellow berries, and nibbled the hulls off a few of them, and then began filling the box. I heard Miss Rossie say to her husband, "Hurry, dear, before the eggs are cold." I came silently into the kitchen and almost bumped into Mr. Lee, fresh from his shave and shower.

"Hello there, Mingie," he greeted me. "I suppose it's you who made the breakfast today."

"Yessuh. I mean, no suh," I said and still didn't explain that I was Veanie, not Mingie. I was afraid deep inside, afraid that I would not be permitted to stay.

When Mr. Lee left for his office, Mrs. Lee saw him off and then came back to the kitchen. "Come and have your breakfast, Mingie," she said. "After we get the house all nice and clean, I'll make you and Veanie dresses out of some material I have."

I lost no time getting to the table. There was plenty for breakfast; there always was plenty at every meal in that house, but I couldn't know that then. I left my plate mirror-clean and reluctantly abandoned the table. I went about cleaning up in the kitchen while Miss Rossie bathed and fed Edie and dressed her in a little checkered sunsuit. Then she went out on the side porch where she had her sewing machine and soon she called to me, "Mingie, bring me the scissors, please."

"Yessum." I hunted for them silently but couldn't find them—perhaps because of a more compelling object that filled my hungry stare. When she called to me again, I could not answer. I heard her rise, and became frantic. "Mingie, can't you find the scissors? Don't you remember, honey, where you—"

Then she saw me seated in a corner of the breakfast nook, hands full of food from the refrigerator, cheeks bulging.

She looked at me and sighed. "Now, Mingie, I must take you home at once. Don't you remember anything we talked about yesterday?"

My eyes rose unsteadily to hers, and I couldn't say a word. "Do you, Mingie?"

At last I found my voice. "No—noam. That wasn't me."

"You—you aren't—?"

"No—noam. I'm Veanie."

"I see." She smiled and touched me very gently and left me to finish my stolen food, which now choked me. When she returned, she spoke to me, as she had to Mingie, of honesty, truthfulness, and good behavior, and how God wanted all little girls to be pleasing in His sight. Mingie had told me this last night, but it was different when it came from Miss Rossie. Somehow, she seemed very near to God, and Mingie wasn't, not any nearer than I was.

I asked her something that Mingie and I had often debated together: "Is—is God white?"

She looked at me and she needed a little time for that. "Wait a minute, honey," she said. "I'm going to put the baby to bed for her nap."

When she returned, she said, "Veanie, honey, we don't know what color God is—or whether He has a color at all. He is more a spirit."

I see her, leaning against the kitchen cabinet as she talked to me.

"A ghos'?" I asked.

"No, just the spirit of goodness and love. And he doesn't look at us to see what color we are. He looks into our hearts to see if we are good and kind."

I looked down doubtfully to where I thought my heart was. She must have realized that I could not fully understand what she had said, but she was not an exhorter, like Aunt Tiller; Miss Rossie never pressed anything on anyone. She put an arm about my shoulders and walked me to the porch where she had been measuring the blue-striped material for two new dresses for Mingie and me.

"Honey, why didn't you tell me you were Veanie? I forgot it was your day to come here," she said, and cuddled me a little.

I grinned, I was feeling so good. Gone was the fear that I might be sent away. "I don' noam," I said.

"Now I'll cut out your dresses."

Saturday was payday. All through the week Mingie and I had discussed how much Mrs. Lee might give us. Fifty cents was the topmost we expected, and we argued what we'd do with it.

We both knew what we ought to do—make a payment on the rent. It was behind; it was always behind, sometimes as much as four dollars—eight weeks. We were used to the rent man's threats, and he was used to our excuse: "But we ain' got no money, an' Papa can' work." He knew that, of course. He also knew that, when matters were at their worst, Aunt Tiller would have the church take up a collection for us. She'd done that again so recently that we owed for only four weeks—two dollars.

"Mingie, how much o' the fifty cents you gonna give me?" I asked. I knew she would be the one to get the money.

"I ain' gonna give you none. You'd spen' it an' we ain' gonna spen' it. We gonna save it in the tin can for the rent man."

"I ain' gonna save my part. Um gonna spen' it an' buy me a whole cake."

"You ain't neither, Veanie. If you is, I won' give you none of it."

"If you don' give me none, um gonna tell Mis' Rossie."

"You can' tell her nothin' 'cause I foun' her," Mingie boasted; she always held that over me.

Saturday was my day to look after Papa, and I could hardly wait for Mingie's return. Mrs. Lee drove her home. When the now familiar car came into sight, I ran out to meet it. Mingie hopped down and we both glued our eyes on Mrs. Lee as she opened her purse.

She took out a dollar bill. "Here, Mingie. You've been a real good help."

"O-o-e-e-e! A whole big dollar! Thank ya, ma'am."

"And here's yours, Veanie—"

I nearly snatched the bill from her hand.

"Don' take it like that, Veanie," Mingie reproved me. "Say: Thank ya, ma'am."

I said it, and in another minute I was helping Miss Rossie and Mingie unload a box of groceries, canned soup, and two bottles of milk.

"Be sure to let Aunt Tiller make your papa's soup," Miss Rossie said as she waved good-by to us and drove off through the heavy sand.

We squeezed our precious dollar bills tightly in our fists, then we ran inside to show Papa our money. He tried to speak, but couldn't. All he could do was to look from Mingie to me and wave his good hand a little, and he tried to smile.

I like to think that then Papa began to understand what a friend and protector we had found and that, as he lay there helpless through his miserable days and nights, his mind was made easier when he thought of us.

5

IT WAS Mingie's day at Mrs. Lee's but she had been sent home because of storm warnings broadcast on the radio. All over the town people rich and poor, white and colored, hurried home or to the solid church or schoolhouse. Mingie and I were busy nailing down our broken window shutters, stuffing up holes, and fastening the doors as firmly as we could.

"If Papa was weller," Mingie said, "we could go out to the schoolhouse where Aunt Tiller an' all them other people is goin'."

"Yeah, but he can' walk and we can' tote him," I pointed out unnecessarily.

Mingie and I often said out loud what other people said to themselves or didn't bother to say at all. Perhaps some identical twins communicate with hardly more than a look or a gesture, but Mingie and I had been lonely and frightened for many years and each of us found comfort and company in the other's voice.

With night the rain came. It came suddenly and beat down

on the tin roof so hard that it sounded like a million tin pans being peppered with gravel. Papa, with a tremendous effort, struggled to get out of bed, but he could only pull himself up a little and motion with his better hand.

Mingie ran to him. "Don' worry none, Papa. We gonna keep you and ourselfs all right. Me and Veanie know how."

I touched his face to find if there were any tears, then patted his arm. Its flesh was rough and dry but the muscles were still hard; he had been a strong man.

"You gonna be all right, Papa," I said, "an' we gonna be all right. Mis' Rossie say it ain' gonna be no big bad storm this time 'cause the man on the radio say it ain't."

"Yeah, Papa," said Mingie. "The radio man say the real big wind is gonna go round the Eas' coas'."

But the radio man was wrong. Hours later Mingie and I hugged together in our bed. The wind was howling and our little house was straining, shivering and complaining in every crack and joint. The night was totally black.

After a while Mingie said, "Veanie, can' you turn me loose? Um hot in here."

"Um scared. Mingie, you—you scared?"

"Yeah."

"Reckin Mis' Rossie's house shakin' like ourn?"

"No. Her house is strong an' she got shetters so the win' can' git in."

"You reckin she scared too, Mingie?"

"No, she ain't scared of nothin', I bet."

"I don't want nothin' to scare her."

"Yeah. An' Edie."

"An' Mr. Lee too."

"Yeah. Now go to sleep, Veanie."

Mingie pushed me away. When I heard her breathing regularly, I slept.

56

A violent wrench of the roof aroused me. "Mingie! Mingie!" I cried as I sprang up. "Feel like the house gonna fall down!"

Mingie was beside me. "O-o-e-e-e!"

We heard a great clattering and banging outside. The zinc tub out in the wash shelter had been swept from its bench and was being tumbled clear across the yard.

Mingie gasped. "That the tub."

Suddenly there was a fearful ripping noise. We smelled the rain and heard it drumming with a new sound. It was in the house! We groped for the matches and somehow, when the wind went down for half a minute, lit the kerosene lamp and carried it in to Papa. He was moaning.

"You all right, Papa?"

He patted his cover. It was wet through. Part of our roof had been ripped off, and although Papa lay under what was left of it, the rain was dripping down on him from a leak right over his bed.

Mingie set the lamp in the most protected place, and together we dragged the bed to the dry corner of the room. We gave Papa our own cover and stayed with him, and in the light of the lamp watched the gusty rain falling on our floor and making rivulets and little pools on the uneven boards.

The rain almost stopped for a while, but not the wind. When Papa fell into a doze, we returned to our room where we found that our own bed was getting soaked. We pulled it to the drier side of the room and got in, wet as it was—there was nothing else to do—and at last we went to sleep again.

I awoke shivering. But it was hardly raining at all and the wind had lessened. Mingie was sitting up and I asked her, "It done stop?"

"No, it ain' stop real good yet."

"Is it near day now?"

"I don' know, Veanie." Mingie thought a moment. It was

dark, but not black. "It feel like mornin'," she decided. "We gotta warm up somethin' to eat. Git up."

We splashed across the floor to the back room. Papa was awake and was all right. The stove was under the part of the roof that had held. We dropped in sticks of wet wood and stuffed in the driest rags and paper we could find. Mingie dashed in a cupful of kerosene. She succeeded in lighting the stove and then ordered me: "Veanie, you wipe up the water while I cook."

I thought it was silly to try to mop up all that water when it was still raining some. Mingie, it seemed to me, was becoming too—too housewifely for our old cabin and old easy ways, like a grown woman. But I went to work.

Almost suddenly, the sky was black again. The wind rose and its sound deepened to something like a roar. We just stood there, too scared to move. We heard the terrible ripping noise again, and then the wind and the rain swooped down. We no longer had any roof at all.

"Mingie!" I shrieked. "The stove poppin'!"

Mingie stared at the steaming and spitting hot iron and backed away. We hugged together.

"Poor ole Papa," said Mingie in my ear. "This house gonna fall down an' he can' walk."

"We all git killed?" I asked.

"We might, sho' 'nough."

High over our heads objects were flying through the air. One we made out was the roof of Aunt Tiller's house. We heard it, or something else, crash far off.

"Don' look no more, Veanie. It make you too scared," said Mingie, holding me tightly. But we both had to look.

When the storm blew itself out, we were sitting on Papa's bed. With us beside him, he didn't groan or try to move, but just waited quietly, as we were waiting. We stirred and grinned, and he waved his good hand. We were wet and cold through and through, Papa and Mingie and I. But we were unhurt, and the shell of our shack still stood. We jumped up and ran to see what the world looked like.

"O-o-e-e-e! All that water!"

The yard was a pond knee-deep. On it floated boards, buckets, tubs, shoes, rags of clothing, branches, and all sorts of broken things.

"Look at all them housetops off!"

"You reckin Mis' Rossie's house got the top blowed off too, Mingie?"

"N-no," said Mingie, and then voiced the deep fear in both of us: "Um sure hope she ain' killed."

"Wish—wish she come now, Mingie." I was wishing it so hard that I felt she must surely appear this very moment, just to let us know she was alive. But I knew that in the white town as well as in ours the hurricane must have so strewn the streets that no car could move.

The day was wearing on, the sky darkened into night with a drizzle of rain from which we had no protection. We opened a can of soup for Papa but we had to spoon it to him cold; the stove had toppled over.

The night was long and wretched. We sat on a box beside Papa until I swayed, and Mingie saved me from falling. We crawled back into our wet bed and shivered together until we warmed a little. All my fears came back, and with them a new one worse than any of the old: Miss Rossie hadn't come. Miss Rossie was hurt, maybe dead!

We were up early. We opened another can of soup and shared it with Papa. The water had lowered in the yard. I was wading in it, looking for things that might be useful, when Mingie shouted: "Veanie! Veanie! Oh, here she come!"

She had stopped her car on the far road, the shell road. She was standing on the running board, looking for a route across the deep pools and the muddy wastes. We screamed and danced, and she waved to us gaily. She had on tall rubber boots. She stepped down, turned, and lifted from the car a big wicker basket covered with a white cloth. Carrying it, she strode through the trashy water, the puddles and ponds and the mud like—God might come like that!

"Hello!"

Gone was the blinding vision and in its place stood a woman nearer and dearer. Mrs. Lee had come and she was the same as always; the lovely, quietly smiling, matter-of-fact Miss Rossie.

"Hello, there. Did the storm almost blow you away?"

"Yessum, an' it blowed the house 'bout down." In happy excitement and sudden pride in our damage, I was making the worst of it. Mingie cut in, "No it didn't, Mis' Rossie. Jus' the roof an' a piece of the kitchen."

"Well, I'm glad it's no worse. Is your father safe too?"

"Yessum, Papa safe."

Mrs. Lee carefully set her hamper on the wreck of the porch. "Has he had something to eat?"

We explained. Mrs. Lee climbed up. "I've brought him something hot. May I go in?"

To this question Mingie always responded with a gracious dignity that filled me with awe: "Yessum, you can go in."

From the porch we heard her talking to Papa. We sat very still, one on each side of the basket, in order to keep ourselves from plunging into it. At last she came out and drew off the cloth. Our eyes bulged, but we made no move.

From a thermos bottle she filled a bowl with steaming soup and handed it to Mingie. "You run in and help your Papa, then come and have breakfast with Veanie. I'm going away now to get dry bedding."

"The roof o' yo' house ain' blow off, Mis' Rossie?" I asked.

"Oh, no. We did have some damage, but nothing like that."

"Is yo' baby all right?"

"Yes." She smiled at me lovingly. "Everyone's all right."

Aunt Tiller came sloshing through the puddles. Her rheumatism was crippling her more than usual. She peered after the departing car. "That yo' boss lady was here?"

"That Mis' Rossie, Aunt Tiller."

"God bless 'er! God bless 'er!" said Aunt Tiller reverently, tears in her tired, pouchy eyes.

"She say she comin' back."

"God bless 'er!"

Now we had food to share with Aunt Tiller who had none. We were proud; we felt like ladies.

When Mrs. Lee returned, she brought not only bedding but many other things, and a man she had hired to repair our house. He gathered boards and sheets of tin roofing that were lying about everywhere. He climbed and crawled about for days. I was fascinated by the way his mouth sprouted nails while he hammered. He made us a roof good as new, and shutters. He set big stones under the house where the floor sagged. He replaced termite-riddled boards with sound ones and he even repaired the stove. He made the whole shack stronger and more solid than it had ever been; he made it a proper house.

Mrs. Lee had had a doctor examine Papa. Now she brought him on a second visit. He said that Papa was the same as before, that his ordeal by storm had apparently not harmed him; but no one could know for certain. Papa might improve, he might not.

Mingie and I talked about it; would we have a well Papa again one day? We remembered him as he had been and hoped that he would not take another wife when he was up and about. The thought was too painful, so we talked about the storm and how Papa had tried to get out of bed when the rain came down. Mingie couldn't get over that. She didn't have the words but she conveyed to me what she felt: Papa was a prisoner, a prisoner in a body that was worse than useless.

Mingie made Papa her special care. She became more adept than I in washing, handling, and feeding him. We would call Aunt Tiller when we needed help; Papa was too heavy for the two of us when it came to changing the bed linen. Besides Aunt Tiller there was another neighbor who sometimes helped us—old, white-bearded Mr. Pem, who was an important man because he had a horse and wagon. He couldn't do much but he came when we needed him.

A few days after the hurricane a revival meeting began at the church. Aunt Tiller harangued us, telling us to go to the meeting. God, she said, had been good to us far beyond our deserts since we didn't have religion. Mingie seemed thoughtful after Aunt Tiller left and I felt uneasy when I looked at her.

"Mingie," I said, "help me bathe Papa before I go to Mis' Rossie. You know she gonna ask me if we done it; an' she don' look at me so good when I tell her we ain'. An' when we ain', I have to say we ain'."

I sighed. There were decided drawbacks to truthtelling.

While we were bathing Papa, Mingie said what I was afraid she would say: "Veanie, les's go to the church tonight and get deligion. I bet Mis' Rossie be real glad, don' you?"

"Um scared," I said. "Um scared at them white things people say they see when they got deligion."

"I ain' scared o' no ole ghos'," Mingie declared. "Mis' Rossie say there ain' no such things. She say it jus' 'magination."

I hadn't heard Mrs. Lee say that, but then I couldn't talk with Miss Rossie as Mingie did. I agreed to go. Aunt Tiller was going to stay with Papa. She was pleased with us. She came at sundown, and by then I had changed my mind, I wanted to stay home. But Aunt Tiller wouldn't have it. "Ya sister is right, gal. Ya get outa here an' go to church an' try ta save ya soul." I trailed Mingie down the road, looking about me for ghosts.

We were early. The small church was still closed and we sat on the step. Soon the preacher and two deacons came and opened the door. One of the deacons lighted the kerosene lamps. The other pulled the heavy rope that swung the big rusted bell overhead. The metallic clangor made me think of the tolling of that bell when somebody died; we often heard it from our porch. But people were coming in now and sitting down.

"We got to get on the mourner bench an' pray, if we gonna get deligion," Mingie said.

"Shucks, Mingie, ya ain' gonna get nothin', nohow." I was annoyed with her. "Only grown people get the real deligion."

"Um is," said Mingie confidently and led the way down the aisle.

Soon the little frame building was full of people singing and clapping their hands as they sang. Mingie clapped and sang right along with them, bouncing on the bench. I just sat.

Suddenly the elderly woman beside Mingie gave a yell, sprang from the bench and began to jerk in a kind of dance, shouting and screaming. It scared me. Then Mingie jumped up and jigged and hollered along with her. By and by Mingie stopped and flung herself across the bench. I was frightened and a woman caught hold of her. But from all over the church came cries: "Let 'er shout!" "Let 'er shout!" "When the spirit hit you, you got to shout!" Mingie rose and shouted some

63

more, and the whole church rocked with the rhythm of stamping feet and clapping hands.

I sat still, shivering. I was afraid Mingie would hurt herself. I was afraid, too, that she was seeing some ghosts. At the same time I was envious. There she was, getting religion right before my eyes. I didn't want to be a sinner. I wanted to go "the straight way" like Mingie looked to be headed for—but to get up there before all these people and fling myself about and scream—! I just couldn't.

When the din died down, leaving a few people weeping, the preacher called for all who felt they were forgiven for their sins to come and tell their determination to live better lives. Mingie was the first to go, and I found myself walking behind her. The preacher and Mingie talked quite a while, and then he shook her hand. The church roared approval. Then I was facing the preacher myself, all alone, and I couldn't say a word. Tentatively I held out my hand. He grasped it. "Veanie," he said, "are you sure you're truly converted?"

"Ye-yessuh."

"You prayed for forgiveness and you feel you got it?"

"Ye-yessuh," I managed. "He done forgive me fo' my sins."

"God bless you!"

On the way home I walked along slowly behind Mingie. At last I gathered courage. "Mingie, did ya see anythin'?"

She stopped. "No. I ain' saw nothin'. You?"

"No, me neither," I said. "But felt like somethin' teched me there in the church and hel' me down and I got real scared."

For a moment we stood in the moonlight staring at each other. Finally I said, "Mingie, you reckin we got any deligion?"

"I don' know 'bout you, Veanie, 'cause you didn' shout none, like I did." She turned and went on. I followed close behind feeling miserable. I had failed Mingie, I had failed God.

At the steps, Mingie stopped again. "Veanie, um goin' real early tomorrow an' tell Mis' Rossie. You come too?"

I wouldn't have anything to tell Miss Rossie. I hadn't thought of that! "Yeah—guess so," I said.

Mingie flew up the steps and ran to Aunt Tiller. "I got deligion, Aunt Tiller!" She began to sob. "I got deligion!"

Aunt Tiller hugged her and wept too. "Thank de Lord, thank de Lord! God knows I'm glad for ya, chile. He'll take care ya. He'll lead ya through. Yeah, my chile. He'll guide ya ever' step o' th' way."

Her eyes searched my face. "What o' you, chile? Is you saved too?"

"Ye-yessum, Aunt Tiller," I said as confidently as I could. "I been born again."

"But Aunt Tiller," Mingie told her, "Veanie didn' shout none."

Aunt Tiller pulled herself up with her crooked stick and called me before her. "Well, now, is ya sure, chile? This ain' nothin' to play 'round with, honey. If ya got nothing', ya better go somewhere an' git on ya knees an' pray."

The next morning we went together to Mrs. Lee's. Mingie was so eager that she trotted almost all the way. She was first up the back steps. Mrs. Lee was in the kitchen. "Mis' Rossie! Mis' Rossie!" cried Mingie, breathless. "We got deligion!" She told all about the meeting and how she had been saved from her sins.

"That's very nice, Mingie," said Mrs. Lee. "I'm so happy for you and Veanie." And then, noticing my silence, she said, "Veanie, how about you? Did you get converted too?"

I looked at Mingie, secure in her greatness, and ventured, "Ye-yessum."

"But she didn' shout none," said Mingie, "an' I did. So

65

maybe Veanie got nothin'. Look, Mis' Rossie—here is how I done las' night."

I thought for one moment that Mrs. Lee was going to laugh at the way Mingie was jumping about and shouting, but maybe that was because I wanted it so hard. I hadn't been saved; I was wishing something mean for Mingie. I was wicked.

Mrs. Lee gravely watched Mingie's performance to the end. She turned away and stood at the screen door, not looking out, just standing there.

When she faced us again, she said, "Maybe Veanie was converted too, Mingie. Maybe she couldn't show her feelings in the same way you did. No two people, not even twins, are alike. If Veanie just felt in her heart that she wanted to be better than before, I'm sure it didn't make any difference to God that she couldn't shout. So Veanie, if you really feel deep down in your heart that you're changed, you are. Do you feel that way?"

"Yessum," I replied, much more confidently.

"Then I'm sure you are, and I'm quite as happy for you as I am for Mingie."

6

IT WAS TRUE that we had changed. But the change didn't begin at the revival meeting of the night before. It began when Miss Rossie came into our lives, and hunger and fear went out.

In the first week we knew her Miss Rossie went through the part of her garage she used for storing things away. She brought out a bed for Papa, a second bed for Mingie and me, a little cedar chest for our clothes and the bed linen she gave us, and a small desk-table. They were the usual housewife's discards, too good to be thrown away but not good enough any more for the house. Mr. Pem came from colored town with his horse and wagon and brought these priceless new possessions to our cabin. Once they were in place, their effect on Mingie staggered me. Our shack wasn't good enough for them, she insisted; we must make it good enough.

Little by little I became willing to do my share of the scrubbing, cleaning, and tidying, in spite of splinters and the long hauls from the community well. We wore our own path to that pump a quarter of a mile away, fetching water.

Mingie decided we must have a walk leading up to our front steps, like Miss Rossie's—a long smooth walk with trees and flowers and shrubbery along the sides.

"But we can' git no cemen'," I pointed out.

Of course she knew that. She reminded me of a bottle path we had seen somewhere and how pretty we had thought it. It had been made of old-style green and bay-colored bottles buried neck down in the sand so that the bottoms, a little above the level of the ground, made a shining track.

We spent weeks of our free time gathering the bottles. We scraped and dug holes in the sandy topsoil, setting a bottle in each hole and every day taking out the bottles and digging deeper and setting them in again to keep the holes from filling up all by themselves. It was a mysterious way they had, we early discovered. We worked very hard. We had to make even rows to begin with. Then, when all the bottles were planted, it was even harder to level them. They seemed to have a will of their own. Some would not go down far enough no matter how deep we dug their holes; others went down a little too far.

At last we could do no more. We gathered pebbles from the railroad tracks and filled the spaces between the bottles.

Mingie stood on the porch and looked down our walk. I stood at the beginning of our walk and looked up it. The late sun, slanting between us, shone on the green and yellow-brown glass. We grinned at each other, and that was enough. For once we didn't have to talk.

It was a long time before the bottles wore even from our coming and going, and often we stubbed our toes or tripped on them. But we were very proud of our walk, and Miss Rossie said it was pretty and a very neat job. She gave us cuts of croton to plant along the sides, but they died in the sandy soil. We set out periwinkles, which grow everywhere in that part of Florida, and hibiscus between the periwinkles.

I remember Mingie on our bottle path trying to walk like Miss Rossie. She said Miss Rossie had a "sporty" walk and she was going to practice until she looked just like her. I wanted to look like Miss Rossie too, but after the first few evenings I gave up and sat on the steps to watch Mingie practicing and to tell her if her shoulders swayed like Miss Rossie's. But Mingie looked so funny bobbing up and down trying to achieve Miss Rossie's little bounce that I'd begin to laugh, and I'd laugh to tears, and Mingie would get angry.

We made a shelf for the wonderful little things Mrs. Lee gave us: a chipped figurine, a vase, a pretty bottle. I remember the china bird, pink, blue, and green, with outstretched wings. Edie had knocked it from the center table and a tip of one wing had broken off. Mrs. Lee mended it and gave it to Mingie.

I was on the porch watching for Mingie to come home. When she came into sight, she began to run, waving a paper sack. I ran to meet her and accidentally caused her to drop the sack. Trembling, she took out the beautiful bird. The mended wing tip had fallen off and the other wing had broken too. Mingie cried about it, but we stuck the pieces on with a flour paste I mixed. In a day or two both pieces had fallen off again, and in time we stopped trying to paste them on. But we loved our bird all the same.

One afternoon Mrs. Lee gave me a pair of thin ecru curtains that were slightly stained. On Saturday Mingie and I, sharing the cost out of our weekly two dollars, bought four yards of pink-flowered cretonne at fifteen cents a yard. We cut two panels to go with the curtains, and Mrs. Lee let us do the hemming on her machine. Mingie, who was better at sewing than I, made a ruffle to go across the top. We strung the curtains on rope which we tied around nails and had the prettiest front windows—or so we thought—of anyone in our part of town.

I remember the day we were hanging our curtains. I was on a box, holding them up for Mingie, when we heard the two quick toots of a horn, Mrs. Lee's signal. I jumped to run out to meet her. The box tilted and I crashed to the floor. I wasn't much hurt but I began to cry because Mingie had got out before me and because I wanted Miss Rossie to make a fuss over me. When she came in, I was still sitting on the floor making the tears come.

She smiled at me. "Get up, Veanie, and let me see. Why, that box isn't high. You can't be hurt much."

I made a great thing of getting up, pretending I was terribly hurt.

Mrs. Lee began to admire the curtains.

Pitifully I held out my bruised arm.

"Oh, you didn't even break the skin, did you?" Mrs. Lee said, and helped us with the curtains.

She knew children. She gave us the strength of her sympathy when it was needed, but never did she let us feel sorry for ourselves. And so were saved from carrying through our lives the sodden burden of self-pity.

When school was about to open, Mingie and I were again telling her about how mean the children had been to us, laughing at us and calling us names. The more we talked, the more mistreated we felt.

"They didn't intend to hurt you," she said. "All children do those things sometimes."

Mingie and I looked at each other and looked away. We were remembering how we had attacked the boy and stolen his lunch pail. And we remembered how, when we had decided not to go back to school ever again, we had plotted revenge on the school bully, our greatest tormentor. One trick of his was to tie us together with his sweater, lift our dresses over our heads, and have the other children douse us with cold water. He was older and bigger than we were, but there were two of us. We ambushed him on his way home from school and pulled his legs from under him and one of us pelted him with sand while the other beat him with a stick until his face was smeared with blood.

No one, not even Miss Rossie, could take from us the savage satisfaction of our revenge; all the same, it was better not to tell her about that incident. Even though she'd said herself, all children do these things sometimes. . . .

We started school again, Mingie going one day and I the next. Mrs. Lee had talked to the principal and obtained permission for the unusual arrangement.

Mingie on her day and I on mine wore our pink-checked dresses, rose-colored socks, and black patent slippers. After school we compared notes. The first two days the other children gathered round and wanted to touch our new clothes. We wouldn't let them and we wouldn't play for fear of getting dirty.

On the third day Mingie told me about the little girl who had been sneering at us for thinking ourselves so cute. There was a scuffle and Mingie didn't mind that, only the damage to one of her socks. When I saw the dirtied sock, I was as angry as she was. I hurried home from school the next day, as we had planned, and Mingie and I got into our old clothes and ran off before Aunt Tiller could know what we were up to—she seemed to have a sixth sense. We caught up with our enemy as she was crossing the railroad tracks. Mingie held her. I rubbed sand and pebbles in her face and made her get down on her knees and swear she would never be mean to us again.

We didn't tell Mrs. Lee about that either, but I think she knew. She knew from the beginning, certainly, that we were not little angels. We were children.

What Mrs. Lee did for us was the wonder of all our neighborhood and, in a different sense, of hers. I was working in her garden one day when two white women came by. One of them said, speaking loudly for me to hear, "That's one of the little niggers Rossie Lee is giving notions to."

It was true. Miss Rossie was giving us notions—of truth and honor and character, along with the notion, strange to us until now, that if we tried hard enough each of us might make herself of some account.

But what the white woman said made me feel sick inside. Because of Papa and Mingie and me, Miss Rossie was being criticized by her neighbors. We racked our brains to think of some way of getting back at her but gave it up.

On a quiet summer afternoon I was alone with Papa. For some time he had been losing strength, but we had become used to that and had stopped worrying about it. But Aunt Tiller came and when she looked at Papa, she stayed.

Papa kept struggling to say something.

"You want th' doctor, Papa?" I asked him again and again. He could shake his head to show it wasn't that.

"Seem to me like he wan' to tell ya somethin' 'bout yo Mis' Rossie," Aunt Tiller said.

I was getting scared about Papa and was mighty glad when Mingie came home. It had been her day in school but, instead of going straight to Mrs. Lee's when school was out, she came home. How had she known? It was almost as if my fear had reached out to her. But more likely she had noticed something about Papa that morning that I had not.

Papa was still struggling to speak. Mingie tried to make out what he was trying to say, but couldn't. Frightened, she ran off to Mrs. Lee's.

It was terrible to stand there watching Papa. I ran to Mrs. Lee's too. I came in hot and panting for breath. Mingie was quietly watching Mrs. Lee dressing her baby.

"Hello, Veanie," said Mrs. Lee in her calm pleasant way.

The house was so peaceful, cool, and sweet-smelling. Nothing, it seemed to me, could ever disturb it or Mrs. Lee.

"Papa, he real, real sick!" I blurted out.

"Yes, honey. Mingie's been telling me. Is Aunt Tiller staying with him?"

"Yessum."

"I'm going to leave Edie with my mother and go back with you."

What tiny details register in the mind at such a time and remain through all the years! One is the click of Miss Rossie's heels on our bottle walk. Another is her white hand on the red hibiscus. "Your plants are growing lovely, Mingie," she said. Inside me, I was crying, "Oh hurry, hurry, hurry, Mis' Rossie!" Now I understand that she must have needed that moment to gather her strength before going in to Papa.

Old Mr. Pem was there with Aunt Tiller beside Papa's bed. He stepped aside for our Miss Rossie. "How is he?" she asked in her low gentle voice.

"Don' think he gonna make it, ma'am," Aunt Tiller whispered.

"No, ma'am." Old, bearded, and wrinkled, Mr. Pem shook his hatted head; he always wore his hat. "He ain' goin' through, ma'am. He done had two of them strokes already. This the third one an' that's all. They's always on'y three."

Miss Rossie's eyes were on Papa, rigid under his blanket except for a twitch now and then. "I'd better go for the doctor," she said.

"Ain' no doctor gonna do him no good," Aunt Tiller said dolefully.

"He dyin' now," said Mr. Pem.

Mrs. Lee drew us close to her, trying to shield our faces. "It's all right, honies," she said. "It's all right."

Papa seemed to recognize her voice. He tried desperately, terribly, to speak. His mouth opened.

His mouth remained open. His lower jaw sank to his neck. The right side of his face pulled tightly into coarse wrinkles, leaving the eye above stretched wide open and ghastly. The twitching ceased, the strain on the muscles relaxed, the pupils rolled upward.

Papa was dead.

A weak gasp from me broke the solemn silence.

Mrs. Lee led us to the front room. We stared at each other and then up at her. We didn't say anything to her; we didn't need to. And when she spoke, it was to our faithful old Aunt Tiller: "I'll take the children home with me for tonight."

I see her at the cemetery, Mingie clinging to one of her hands, I to the other. The fresh grave gapes before us. A big gray box rests on ropes stretched over the deep hole. Two silent men begin to lower the box by the ropes. But they can't, they can't! Papa is in that box, nailed in! I jerk to run away, but Mrs. Lee looks down at me and her eyes and her hand hold me. A sudden, heavy rain comes down, tapping and beating on the box like a drum. Soon we are standing in muddy water.

Slowly, slowly the box goes down. Now and then Mrs. Lee takes her hand from Mingie's or mine and brushes back the golden-brown strands of hair blown against her temples and plastered there by the rain; always she gives back her hand again.

The lowering stops. The preacher scoops up a handful of mud and tosses it on the box. "Ashes to ashes and dust to dust." The "dust" is a muddy rill running down the side of Papa's coffin.

The box is down. The ropes are loosened and pulled up from under it.

I begin to sob with grief and terror. "Papa! Papa!"

Mingie blinks up at Mrs. Lee and doesn't cry; Mingie tells me not to. "Don' cry, Veanie. Mis' Rossie say our papa restin' now."

"Yeah, honey, don' cry 'bout him." Old Aunt Tiller is leaning heavily on her crooked stick. "He gone to everlastin' peace. God knows best. He'll take care of ya."

Mrs. Lee drove us home. Aunt Tiller and Mingie and me. When we got into the car, for a while Mingie and I busied ourselves brushing the water from each other's black ribbon bows and white cotton dresses that Mrs. Lee had made us for the funeral. The sudden shower was over and the warm sun brought out the heavy, sweet smell of the guava and sapodilla trees.

In the palmetto scrub Mrs. Lee stopped the car; Aunt Tiller thanked her and got herself to the ground and limped up the worn path to her house. Mrs. Lee came with us to our cabin.

"Run in and put on dry clothes," she said, "and bring a fresh dress for school." In this way she was telling us that she was taking us home with her again.

Mingie hopped down. I just sat.

"Aren't you going to change, honey?" Mrs. Lee asked me.

"Oh, yessum. I was almost forgettin'. I was thinkin' it my day to stay with Papa."

7

AFTER PAPA'S DEATH we lived with Mrs. Lee for about a week. There was a bed for us in the enclosed part of the back porch. A few more days and we would have frogotten all about our own cabin and considered the Lee home our own. But Aunt Tiller intervened. She said to come back; Papa would have wanted it. She and Mrs. Lee talked about it one day when we came to get some of our clothes, and Mrs. Lee agreed. We needn't be afraid to live alone, she told us—and in fact we weren't. Aunt Tiller, she said, would keep an eye on us.

Aunt Tiller—as I see it now—was wise. She knew we must not impose too much on our Miss Rossie. She also saw how bad it would be to cut ourselves off from the colored community and vainly try to become part of the white. But she never said that.

"Y'all lucky Mis' Rossie help ya th' way she do," Aunt Tiller told us again and again. "Don' y'all bring her no trouble over there—and don' ya get into no trouble here."

We weren't happy about going back to our cabin. All the same, it did seem wrong not to be living there after all we had done to make it pretty. And when we were back, we knew we had missed it. It hadn't been borrowed, it hadn't been given to us—it was our very own. We had a house and we were paying rent just like grown-up folks. We were Somebody.

Mingie and I now went to school together, and after school we went to Mrs. Lee's, and in the evening we came home and did housework and our lessons. Mingie liked the housework better than studying; I liked studying better than housework. Sometimes we got into a quarrel over that and as a result did neither housework nor homework.

It was a Saturday morning about a year after Papa's death; I place it by how big Edie had grown. We had gone to Mrs. Lee's early, as we always did on Saturday. We had brought Edie back from her walk, and I sat in an armchair cuddling her and singing to her.

"Is she asleep now, Veanie?" Miss Rossie asked.

"Yessum."

"She's such a big girl for you all to be still rocking her to sleep."

"I like to rock her."

"But she's heavy."

"Yessum, but she don'—doesn't seem so. Do you want me to lay her down out on the porch where it's cool?"

"No, I'll put her in her room and turn on the fan." She gathered up Edie. "Honey, you run in and help Mingie, will you? We're having company for supper tonight."

Mingie and I perched on our stools in the kitchen, laughing and chattering and rubbing the silver; we loved to see it glitter. Miss Rossie came into the kitchen, and after a moment she said, a little too brightly, "Which of you would like to go help Mrs. Vann?"

There was a silence.

"Mrs. Vann's a good friend of mine," said Miss Rossie, "and she's very nice."

Mingie's eyes met mine in a quick glance, and hers, like mine, fell to the silver. We went on rubbing, without a word.

"How about you, Mingie? Mrs. Vann's the one coming to supper and she knows all about you. She lives near enough so you and Veanie can visit back and forth. Her little girl Patsy is about Edie's age and you all could take them out together—"

"Yeah, you go, Mingie," I said.

"No, you go," my sister returned.

"Suppose you try it, Mingie. In that way you both will have more money," said Miss Rossie, a little desperately. "Won't that be nice?"

I looked at Mingie. "Yeah," I prompted her.

"Ye-yessum," said Mingie reluctantly.

Miss Rossie couldn't keep back a small sigh of relief. It must have been hard on her to have the two of us shrieking and tearing up the back porch and back yard as we often did, romping with Edie. But I think she was also beginning to be concerned about our being always together. She knew we were two, not one; each of us must stand on her own feet; each must go her own way.

So Mingie went to Mrs. Vann's.

A few days later in the afternoon a car pulled into the driveway. Mrs. Vann had come to visit, bringing Patsy and Mingie. I led Edie down the steps, and Mingie came to meet us, letting Patsy trot ahead of her. Patsy's long blond curls bounced on her shoulders. The big yellow satin bow on top of her head matched the gay dress and silk socks she wore with white, four-strap, high-top shoes.

Edie's simple flowered sunsuit and brown open sandals

78

were more suitable than Patsy's party outfit for an afternoon of play. But Mingie and I looked at each other as the little girls met. Then we glanced at the two mothers. Mrs. Lee had gone to the car and was laughing and chatting with Mrs. Vann.

"Come on, Veanie," Mingie said. "Let's go in for a minute."

We led the little girls upstairs, gave each a toy, and sat them on the bed while we searched through Edie's clothes in the closet. We drew out dress after dress, arguing which was the prettiest.

"Put that li'l yellow one on her, Mingie."

"No, it don't have ruffles on it like Patsy's."

"Well, how about this pink one?" I spread the wide fluffy skirt of a little silk dress that was gathered full from the shoulders and had tiny rosebuds embroidered down the front and around the Peter Pan collar.

"No. That's her Easter dress and you know it took Miss Rossie 'bout a month to do all that work on it."

"Just the same, we gonna put it on her," I insisted.

"No, we ain't—aren't."

"Then let's put on this blue one." I held up a crisp organdy party frock.

"All right—an' get her some blue socks out of her draw' an' bring her white high-tops."

"Ribbons too—blue ones."

Carefully, one on each side of her, we led Edie downstairs, leaving Patsy to come along behind. On the porch, Mingie distracted Patsy by giving her one of Edie's dolls.

Edie's little blue figure, dripping ribbons and sporting bows, trotted across the green grass to the car. As the two mothers turned, she spread out her skirts and turned all the way around, like a tiny trained model. Mingie and I exchanged a look of secret triumph.

"Hello, Mistis Bann," Edie said.

The mothers just stared.

"Well!" Mrs. Lee exclaimed in amusement. "Why did you get all dressed up? Because Patsy looks so pretty?"

"Mingie made me pretty," said Edie proudly.

"Mingie?" Mrs. Vann remarked to Miss Rossie. "She doesn't know them apart either, does she?" She said to Edie, "Sweetheart, wasn't it Veanie who put those lovely things on you?"

"No," said Edie. "Mingie."

Mrs. Vann was puzzled. She asked Miss Rossie, "It's Mingie who works for me now, isn't it?"

"Yes, of course," Miss Rossie said, and they both laughed and began to talk of other things.

We took the children to play in the sandbox under the big mango tree. Soon they were scooping and tossing sand at each other. Patsy flung a handful of sand right into Edie's face. Edie screamed, and Mingie and I both jumped for her and took her up. Neither of us noticed that Patsy, sobbing with fright, was scampering off down the driveway as fast as her short legs could carry her.

Miss Rossie caught her up in her arms, and both mothers hurried to where we were petting Edie and trying to get the sand out of her eyes.

"Mingie," said Miss Rossie, "take Patsy."

But Mingie just kept on helping me with Edie.

"Give Patsy to me, Rossie," Mrs. Vann said. "She's not hurt. Come to Mother, darling. Rossie, I'll go to the car and get her quiet."

Miss Rossie knelt beside us. "Mingie," she said, "you should have looked out for Patsy. You didn't at all."

"Yessum—but she threw sand in Edie's face—"

"But Veanie was here for Edie."

"Yessum."

"Come on, now; Mrs. Vann is ready to go."

Mingie lingered a few minutes before rejoining Mrs. Vann and Patsy. As they drove away, Miss Rossie said worriedly, "Doesn't Mingie like to work for Mrs. Vann?"

"Yessum," I said, "she likes it all right."

On the following Saturday morning when Mrs. Lee came down, she found Mingie with me in the kitchen.

"Why, hello," she said in surprise. "What are you doing here today? Shouldn't you be at Mrs. Vann's?"

"Yessum—but Miss Rossie, she said she think she got to have somebody for Patsy all day."

"You mean you aren't going back any more?"

"Yessum."

Miss Rossie looked at her, hesitated a moment, then turned and went out of the kitchen.

I waited until I heard the bedroom door click. "Mingie," I said, "you got to tell her the truth—old lady Vann fired you. You know Miss Rossie said don't never tell no stories."

"I didn't tell no story. She didn't really and truly fire me. She just say, didn't look like I want to work for her, and she need somebody all day long, anyway. She say I don't have to come back if I don't want to."

"Well, you got to tell Miss Rossie all of it."

Mingie just looked away.

The next morning when Mingie and I came, Miss Rossie greeted us as usual and said nothing to Mingie about Mrs. Vann. But Mingie felt uncomfortable.

When we were alone, she said anxiously, "Veanie, you reckon she gonna let me stay?"

I couldn't answer that. I said, "She knows you ain't—you're not—telling all the truth."

After breakfast Miss Rossie went to the side porch to sew. Mingie had been trying to keep out of her way, but soon she called both of us. We saw with dismay that she was very grave. We'd seen her look like that only when one of us, or Edie, had done something bad.

"Mingie," she said, "I talked with Mrs. Vann last night. I was disappointed in what she told me. She said you hadn't seemed satisfied there. I had told her so many nice things about you that I was ashamed."

Mingie had moved behind her to be out of sight. If she could have found a hole to crawl into, she would have done it, and I would have popped in after her. Edie, playing on the floor, understood the tone of her mother's voice. She hugged her doll and looked at us with round blue eyes.

"There are many people in the world. You will have to go out on your own one day and work for other people. You have to think of the future—high school, living expenses, maybe college—"

But Miss Rossie couldn't lecture. She turned in her chair and looked helplessly at Mingie and said, "Honey, I'm only trying to help you!"

"Mis'—Mis' Rossie"—Mingie's voice broke—"I'll go back and work for Mrs. Vann if you want me to. I'll do everything—"

Miss Rossie's eyes were loving. "But not for my sake, Mingie; not just because I wish it."

"But please, Miss Rossie, I want to," said Mingie with all her heart.

Edie got up from the floor and hugged Mingie's legs. "Mimi, I want Mingie, I want Mingie."

"Now hush, young lady, you just take care of your doll."

Edie eyed her for a moment—her Mimi's "bad" look was turned full on her. She went back to her doll.

After a while Miss Rossie said, "Mingie, my sister would like you to take care of her little boy. She said you could come

82

the same as here—after school and on Saturday and part of Sunday until vacation time. You'll earn two dollars a week, just as Veanie does here. Would you like to try it?"

My relief was not just for Mingie. It was for myself even more. I wasn't going to be sent away. I was going to stay on with Miss Rossie.

"Yessum," said Mingie, not looking at me. "Can me and Billie come over every day?"

"Well, not every day but very often."

When we were walking home, I said, "Mingie, Mrs. Porter is Miss Rossie's sister and she'll be just like Miss Rossie to work for."

"She don'—Mrs. Porter doesn't *look* much like Miss Rossie," Mingie said, speaking correctly. Miss Rossie had said we ought to try to talk like that even when there was no one else to hear us. When we remembered, we tried, but we often lapsed. Now we were remembering.

We were being cautious with each other because of the sore point neither of us spoke of: it was Mingie who had found Mrs. Lee and she should have been permitted to stay. *I* should be the one to go.

"No, she doesn't." I had to agree that Mrs. Porter didn't look like Miss Rossie. "But she'll be real nice—I guess." I looked at my sister imploringly, but she didn't say anything.

I said, "Miss Rossie wants us to have lots of money. We'll have four whole dollars, and after we pay half a dollar for the rent, we have three and a half left. And all the food she give us, and you'll get a lot from Mrs. Porter too—"

"And clothes and things," said Mingie, with a rise in spirits. "Why, we don't have to buy nothin', do we?"

"Oh, Mingie," I said, reverting to our old way of talk, "ain' nobody got so much, hardly. Y'know—didn't nobody hardly want to be nice to us till Miss Rossie got us, did they?"

83

Mingie began to smile. "Remember how all th' chil'ren look at us when we come back to school in them pretty dresses?"

"An' they don' call us names like Gol' Dus' Twins no mo', and they like to be with us."

Mingie grinned more broadly. "Veanie, 'member how Mis' Rossie tried to fix your hair first day for school? Didn' know how to do with kinky hair, parted it crooked and tied up th' pieces 'cause she didn' know to plait braids. You looked jus' like somebody put a whole lot of black rags on top your head."

We began to laugh and we laughed so hard we had to hold on to each other.

We sat under the shade of a huge palm tree and went on talking about Miss Rossie.

" 'Member that time how mad she got when ole teacher beat me up 'cause I couldn't say that ole thing—about a bunch of sentences is called a paragraph?"

"But you sure learned it afters, Mingie."

"Yeah, I was scared she'd whip me again."

"She was scared, too, when she found out we told Mis' Rossie."

"Yeah, Mis' Rossie fix it. Veanie, I reckon there just ain't nothin' Mis' Rossie can't fix."

"Mis' Rossie almost like our real mother. Ain'—isn't she, Mingie?"

"Y'know, Veanie," Mingie said, "Mis' Rossie might give me that pretty green dress she bought—said it was too small for her. She might fix it over for me."

"But you won' be working for her no more. Maybe she give it to me."

As soon as I'd said that, I could have bitten off my tongue. But after a moment Mingie said, "I bet Mrs. Porter's real

84

nice. I rather work for her than anybody else but Mis' Rossie."

At peace with each other and with the world, we went on toward home.

Before we reached the part of town near the railroad tracks that marked the boundary between blacks and whites, it was nearly dusk. The smell of rain was in the air. But the grassy bank above the tracks looked so nice and cool and there was nobody waiting for us at home and it felt so good just to be together—Mingie said what I was thinking before I even knew I was thinking it: "Veanie, let's stay till the Coast Line go by."

The train was due in about half an hour. While waiting, we amused ourselves scooping up handfuls of the speckled brown pebbles beside the tracks and seeing which of us could throw the farthest. Mingie found a big stone. She threw it with all her might. A shattering sound split the air.

"Wha'—what's that!" cried Mingie. Frightened, we both stared into the gathering darkness. There was nothing to see, nothing to damage. Had the stone exploded?

Suddenly we heard more of the same sounds, a whole round of them. They seemed to be coming nearer.

"Shootin'!" Mingie grabbed my hand and we bolted down the grassy slope, across the tracks, and down again into the muddy water of the ditch. We crawled into the thick brush and palmetto on the opposite side where we paused for breath.

"Mingie," I quavered, "le's go back to Mis' Rossie."

"Yeah. Come on."

We scrambled to our feet and were about to hop over some rusty barbed wire to the road when we heard automobiles approaching, more shots, yelling, and blaring horns. "Get down, quick," Mingie ordered. "It's a whole bunch o' white people an' they got guns."

We lay together in the scanty shelter of the brush. "You reckon they comin' to kill us 'cause we be up to Mis' Rossie's all this time?" I whispered.

"I don' know," said Mingie, "but some o' th' white people don' like for her to be so nice to us. You know that ole woman up the street say we li'l black niggers an' we got no right ever to go in Mis' Rossie's front door. . . . Here th' train."

The long Coast Line express thundered by, shaking the earth, raising clouds of dust. The autocade had to stop at the crossing. The cars skidded and bumped one another in the rear. Through the settling dust and by the headlights we saw the ugly nozzles of shotguns, rifles, and pistols. We watched angry-faced men race their motors, shouting and swearing. They jerked their cars into action, and as they drove off toward colored town, they fired their guns into the air.

"Mingie, I want Mis' Rossie." I was trembling and crying, and I could feel Mingie shaking too, but she said, "Don' cry, Veanie. We can' go there now. We better stay right here all night and go to Mis' Rossie in th' mornin'. They gonna kill somebody, sure, and might be mo' of 'em comin'."

Mingie herself was crying now, but she wiped her nose with the back of her hand and sat up. "Come on, Veanie, lay yo' head on my lap an' don' cry no mo'."

"But might be snakes here in th' bushes."

'Well, if it is they ain't nothin' but plain ole black snakes, an' if they bite it don' kill you none, Aunt Tiller say."

Then another line of cars came into sight and bumped across the tracks. We heard the men's voices, even angrier than the others, and they swore more furiously.

Mingie and I lay flat on the ground, hugging together.

The night closed down, damp and chilling. We were wet

86

from our plunge into the ditch. I began to cough. "Le's go home, Mingie," I begged her. "When we git home le's go under th' bed."

"Yeah. But we gotta make sure no mo' of 'em comin' so we can git 'cross th' road. If they see us out there—"

"Yeah."

We lay there for a long time. At last we ventured to crawl out of the bushes and up the embankment. We walked along the edge of the tracks, carefully searching out the wooden ties to keep from making a noise on the pebbles. Nearing the dim rim of light from a street post, we heard loud voices again. We slipped behind a clump of tall brush into a shallow ditch. We peered around it. Armed men were stamping through the weeds and palmetto, searching for something—someone. All had guns. One of them, on guard in the road, seemed to have smelled us out. He turned our way and raised his rifle.

"Don' move!" Mingie gasped.

We stood stock-still behind our clump of brush. The man took a step in our direction. We went down flat on our stomachs in the hard, wet sand.

"Veanie, ya gotta stop cryin' else you gonna cough," Mingie whispered urgently. I managed to stop my tears but not my shaking, and Mingie was shivering too.

The men gathered around the light, enraged at not finding what they hunted. One made an awful threat: "If we don't get that black nigger tonight, we'll kill every other nigger in this county!" Voices shouted agreement, and the guns went off again. We saw them "breaking" their weapons and reloading as they walked. At the end of the hard road they crowded into cars and trucks and onto motorcycles they had parked there. We heard the starting up of one motor after another, the angry clash of gears, the sound of the wheels on the shell road of colored town.

We could not move. Only one person could take away our terror, could make us believe that somehow our eyes hadn't seen, our ears hadn't heard, not really.

"Mis' Rossie—Mis' Rossie," I begged for her. "Please, ma'am, Mis' Rossie, come an' get me an' Mingie."

Mingie hugged me. She was praying the same prayer, but she was more practical-minded. "Come on, honey," she said. "We gotta get home 'cause if she come, we won' be there."

"Mingie," I said, "I gotta cough. My throat feels funny."

"Put yo mouth on th' ground an' the soun' will go down in it," Mingie said. I coughed into the damp earth. Hand in hand, stopping now and then to listen, we made for home. From beyond the palmettos we could hear shooting.

Our neighborhood was dark. There was no glint of light, no voice. Every door and shutter was tightly closed. The only movement was the slight swaying of the dog fennels and the leaves of the little guava trees. Suddenly a cat darted in front of us. I would have screamed but my voice came out a harsh, funny croak.

"Black!" I said in a panic. "Mingie, a black cat! We gotta go back!"

I was pulling her but she broke away from me. "Now listen here, Veanie. We goin' home, cat or no cat. Anyhow"—she lied bravely—"it was gray."

So we reached our cabin and tiptoed up to the porch. Mingie shoved open the door. We peered into the pitch-black room. Even Mingie recoiled from that. "Veanie, le's don' go in; that door don' lock, no way."

"We gotta go somewhere," I whispered despairingly. "It gone to rainin' now."

"Le's—le's go under th' house."

I followed Mingie. On hands and knees we crawled among the rusty tin cans and broken bottles under our house. We pawed out a little hollow behind the wooden props. Soon I was asleep, with my head in Mingie's lap.

Noises awakened me and I coughed. "Sh-sh-h!" Mingie clapped her hand over my mouth. "They out there," she whispered.

I could see boots in the pointed glares of flashlights. A man called, "Here, Bill. I think he's under the house. I heard something. Bring that big spotter." He came into my sight as he dropped to his knees. He was hugging a rifle. "Shine it under here," he ordered.

A great round eye of light shone in on us, but in that instant the black cat which I had thought bad luck saved us. He—or maybe it was another cat—darted from behind one of the blocks under the house and streaked off into the brush. "A cat!" the man swore—and rose.

The big spotter stared at us with its evil eye, but the men stamped up our steps and kicked open the door. Not moving, hardly daring to breathe, we listened to them tramping through our two rooms, ransacking, throwing things over.

"Come on, nobody's here." The voice was impatient.

They came down. "Which way?" somebody shouted.

"To the bottom."

The spotter suddenly blinked off, leaving us in blessed darkness. There was a slamming of car doors and the starting up of motors. A truck had trouble getting started, and Mingie and I squeezed each other at every backfire. But at last it was gone, too.

Still we dared not move from the hollow under the house. All night we lay there, shivering uncontrollably. Was it me or Mingie that was shivering so? Or both of us together?

At dawn we crawled out. The world was silent and lifeless. There were none of the familiar morning sounds—talk and laughter, the yell of a baby demanding attention, or a housewife's rattle and bang of stove and pots. We stood looking at Aunt Tiller's house. The shades were drawn; the doors and windows were shut. We stole up the road a little piece. Nothing. Nobody going to work; nobody getting ready for school. All the houses were tightly shut, like Aunt Tiller's. They looked strange that way—blind and frightened.

We ran into our own house and stood at a window, watching for something, waiting. Mis' Rossie! Oh, Mis' Rossie! But we didn't say it. Then from a distance we heard shots again, triumphant shouts, and blaring horns, like a celebration. The autocade was returning.

"Oh lordy, Mingie," I moaned. "Here they come back an' it daytime. They see us now."

Mingie closed the wooden shutter and I fumbled its hook into the loop made by a bent nail. We propped a chair under the knob of the door. We stood glued to cracks in the wall, peering out.

Three crowded cars came into view, and then a faded-green truck. The truck was rigged with barbed wire, ropes, and chains. There in the rigging a dark form tumbled over the bumps and holes in the road. The truck wasn't moving fast; we could see too well the horribly broken thing it dragged—the quarry of the all-night search.

I tried to speak but could only gasp as we hugged together.

A volley of shots sent us back to our watching post. The autocade had stopped for a terrible moment. Then it moved on again to the small business center of colored town.

Much later we ventured out to see what they had done. They had left the mangled carcass suspended from the wooden joists before a store. It was swinging like a ghastly pendulum.

We flew back to the cabin and barricaded ourselves. Then we stood at our cracks, waiting.

An eternity passed. And then my heart gave a great leap. I saw the familiar blue car. "Mingie! Mingie! Here she come!"

Mingie held me back. "Don' go out there, Veanie. We gotta make sure an' see if she really comin' here an'—" She didn't say the rest of it, the terrible fear. What if Miss Rossie was no longer our Miss Rossie? What if she had changed, like so much else had suddenly changed?

We went back to our places, and watched. Miss Rossie stepped from her car. She stood a moment, looking about.

She was coming. She walked in long strides, like always, but more quickly. Somehow she seemed to have lost her gay little bounce. Now she was on our bottle walk, her heels clacking on the still air. Her eyes were straight ahead on our door. Her brows were pinched together in an expression we hadn't ever seen before.

She stopped and called. "Veanie? Mingie?"

That voice, that dear beautiful voice! We scrambled to open the door, and all the coughing I had managed to suppress burst out explosively along with great gulping sobs. Mingie was crying too. "Oh, Mis' Rossie, Veanie's sick. We got wet. We hadda sleep under th' house." Mingie was trying to tell everything at once.

"We saw it, Mis' Rossie," I managed. "They—"

Mrs. Lee had us in her arms. "Veanie, honey, you're awfully hoarse."

"They hung 'im—"

"How would both of you like to come and stay with me tonight so I can work on Veanie's cold?"

"Oh, yessum," said Mingie. "Mis' Rossie, those men—"

"Get Veanie's coat, Mingie, dear. It's hot but she's shivering, we'll have to bundle her up."

Mingie got me into my coat. "Look, Mis' Rossie—how red her eyes is."

"Yes, I see. Come on, now. Hurry." She had me sit in the front seat close beside her. "You'd better sit here with me, Veanie, so the air won't strike you."

Instead of turning around as she usually did, Miss Rossie kept on in the direction her car was headed. It was the longest and roughest route to her house, and Mingie reminded her: "Mis' Rossie, up this road there's lots of big holes. Maybe you get stuck."

"Yes, I know. But I think I can make it."

At the intersection I craned my head out the window. "Mis' Rossie, Mis' Rossie, if you look down that street you might see him hangin'—"

Her eyes never left the road. She said, "Who is it that's so crazy about grits and sausage?"

"Me!"

"Well, that's what we're going to have."

Mingie was saying nothing. I knew she was thinking, as I was: Why doesn't Miss Rossie explain about the killing? Why won't she let us even talk about it?

Except for my coughing, Mingie and I were both silent the rest of the way.

8

"PNEUMONIA," said the doctor. "Better get her to the hospital."

"Mingie," said Mrs. Lee, "you take Edie and go over to Grandma's till I get back. I'll come by for you."

She was wrapping me in a blanket. I was too sick to feel frightened until I heard Mingie: "Mis' Rossie, is Veanie gonna die?"

"Honey, don't think of anything like that. We'll get her well." She helped me out to the doctor's car and sat beside me.

I fought through nightmare after nightmare; I was caught in the lynching and I mustn't say anything about it, not a word. Yet I knew that every day, and often more than once a day, Miss Rossie came. I'd feel her cool hand on mine or on my forehead and hear her gentle voice and then I'd know I was safe in a hospital. Nobody was going to hurt me. I was only sick.

Sometimes I was aware that it was late in the day; she was here with me at the hour when Mr. Lee would be coming home. That worried me. Later I learned from Mingie that he never complained. Perhaps any white man would have cause to think that his wife would be spending too much time with a little black girl who depended so much on her. But not Mr. Lee. He loved her dearly and went along with her wishes.

On the morning of the eighth day of my illness he said to Miss Rossie: "Honey, I suppose you want to be with Veanie today especially, don't you? They tell me the break is coming, for better or worse."

"Yes."

"Well, you go on out there. I'll get my breakfast, and Mingie can get hers and Edie's. I'll call from the office every now and then to see how they are."

The crisis came that very day. Miss Rossie went home in the late afternoon, and Mingie saw her face bright again though she was exhausted.

"Veanie is just fine," she called, her voice ringing musically as it did when she was happy. "The doctor says she can go home soon."

Tired though she was, she would not lie down. She hurried through the cooking, but when Mr. Lee came home she almost broke down in his arms. He held her tightly, and then it was all right. After supper, while Mingie, singing, cleaned the kitchen, Miss Rossie went to the porch to sew. She began to alter one of her silk dresses that had got too small for her. It was for me to come home in.

Miss Rossie talked to me of many things in the hours she sat beside my bed in the hospital. I don't remember them all now. She talked of high school; Mingie and I must go on with our schooling beyond where so many colored children stopped. She had noticed that I had been quietly teaching little Edie

94

numbers and the alphabet. And I remember she spoke for the second time a magic word: college.

But one subject she never mentioned: the lynching. And Mingie and I never again tried to talk to her about it. Quickly we had sensed, and more slowly we digested, a fact that we must sooner or later know: there were some things in the world that even Miss Rossie couldn't "fix." And if she couldn't fix them, she wasn't going to talk about them. That was Miss Rossie's way.

Home again. For a while our old cabin looked just about as beautiful to me as Miss Rossie's house. Aunt Tiller watched over me during the day, Mrs. Lee often looked in to make sure I was having no setback, and evenings Mingie nursed me, fussing around as if I were helpless, like Papa. But Mingie was pleased that my disability gave her my place at Mrs. Lee's.

"Veanie, you reckon I'm gonna have to go to Mrs. Porter's again?" said Mingie. We were lounging on the bed on our back porch looking through some magazines Miss Rossie had brought us.

"Yeah!" It came out in a kind of explosion. I had been worried. I was afraid that Mingie would be staying at Mrs. Lee's now and I would be the one sent to Mrs. Porter.

Mingie eyed me warily. "Well, I guess I'll have to go then."

"So you might just as well get ready!" I said triumphantly, as if the whole matter had been settled.

But we couldn't let it go at that nor could we touch the sore spot—Mingie's being sent off when it was she who had found Miss Rossie—and so we got into a fight about something else. After that Mingie stopped her fussing over me, and I was no longer an invalid.

A few days later Miss Rossie came to say it was time for me

95

to go to school again; I was all well now. She brought a dress she had made over for Mingie; and pink silk panties and a white slip to go with it.

"You'll come back to me, Veanie," Miss Rossie said, "if school doesn't tire you out too much at first. And Mingie, Mrs. Porter is expecting you first thing Monday afternoon. All right?"

"Yessum," said Mingie, careful not to look at me.

But the old trouble between us was forgotten when we heard Miss Rossie, on the way to her car, calling to Aunt Tiller, asking how Mingie and I had been getting along.

"Yessum, Mis' Lee, they doin' real good, ma'am," Aunt Tiller hollered from her rickety rocker on her porch.

We couldn't hear what Miss Rossie said then, but we heard Aunt Tiller promise her, "Yas, ma'am, I sho' will. Yessum. Yessum."

We talked a lot about that, Mingie and I. What was it that Aunt Tiller was sure going to do? We were certain it concerned us. We tried to find out from Aunt Tiller in every way we could, but she was too clever for us.

We never did find out. Not knowing had a good effect on us. We did our school work as never before, and the vague worry that prodded us soon gave way to real pleasure. We had friends at school now, and sometimes in the evening there would be a group of boys and girls on our porch and we'd all be chattering and laughing and singing.

Had we ever been lonely? Long ago two little girls, the dirtiest and most ragged in colored town, had been the target of taunts and bullying. Those little girls had gone. In their place were the neat, well-dressed, diligent and popular Mingie and Veanie Bennett with a house all their own, the distinction of having had pneumonia (somehow Mingie shared in that), and a guardian angel in white town.

The term came to an end. On closing day we streaked out of school and ran all the way to Mrs. Lee's. Mingie could run faster; she got there first. Miss Rossie thought Mingie was me until I came in, panting. When we were together she could tell who was who.

"Why, Mingie," she exclaimed, "haven't you been to Mrs. Porter's today?"

"Oh, yessum—I mean, no, ma'am; not yet. But I'm going. I just came by to tell you—"

"We got skipped!" I put in excitedly.

Mingie took up again. "The principal says we're real smart, we got the best marks, so he skips us to—"

"Seventh! Seventh grade!" I cried.

"When school opens next September," Mingie explained.

"No sixth grade!" I was almost dancing. "We go straight up to seventh with all the big children up there."

Miss Rossie hugged us.

During the school vacation we worked full time, Mingie for Mrs. Porter and I for Mrs. Lee, each of us earning three dollars a week. We had grown in many ways and now we could be much more helpful. Our training in house cleaning, cooking, serving, and looking after Edie and Billie went along painlessly; at least it did for me. I was doing my work, and more, without being told what to do. I began to reach out to other things.

Both Mr. and Mrs. Lee played the piano. Miss Rossie often practiced after lunch, and sometimes in the evening before I went home Mr. Lee would be playing, and then it was very hard to leave. They played the popular hits of the day and sometimes they would listen to them, or to more difficult songs, on the phonograph.

One day Miss Rossie came in when I was picking out a tune on the piano. I had been listening for her—she had gone shop-

97

ping or visiting—but the tune had begun to come right, and I had forgotten it was time for her to be back. I jumped up, frightened, when I saw her standing beside me. But she only said, "That's nice, honey."

"Miss Rossie, ma'am—" I gulped. "Miss Rossie, can I play the phonograph sometimes when you're not home?" I added quickly, "Edie likes it."

She smiled at me but didn't say anything.

"Well," I admitted, "she does, but I like it more, I guess."

She patted my shoulder. "Yes, of course you can play it. Or the piano if you wish."

Miss Rossie was out a lot that summer and she often took Edie with her. One morning a neighbor came calling. I was in the kitchen but I heard her; maybe she meant me to hear. "Rossie, that nigger of yours waits till you're gone and you're hardly out of sight when she's playing your piano or your phonograph!" She was angry.

I couldn't hear what Miss Rossie answered, her voice was too low; but it was pleasant.

When the visitor had gone, Miss Rossie came into the kitchen. She glanced at me and knew that I had heard. "Veanie, honey," she said, "when you want to play the piano or the phonograph just close the windows first, will you?"

Mingie laughed when I told her about it. "I bet that woman thought Miss Rossie would be mad and get at you."

One Sunday morning I stood beside Mrs. Lee at the breakfast table watching each stroke of her thick black pencil as she sketched her husband. The face was coming out clearly.

"Oh, Miss Rossie," I exclaimed, "I wish I could draw like you!"

"Look, honey," she said, "it's not hard. Here's all you have to do." She took a fresh sheet of paper. "First look at his forehead, his nose, his mouth." As she named the features she formed them rapidly. Then, with the pencil held aslant, she skittered with it at different angles inside of the outline. "Now you just shade in the old man's wrinkles," she said as, with a finger, she smudged the lines and scratches, and, where highlights were needed, she removed the darkness with the eraser.

"Well!" Mr. Lee said. "Wrinkles? If he has any wrinkles he's not the gentleman at this table! Let me see, old lady." He reached for the sketch, studied it, and prasied it. "Only, I'm handsomer," he said.

"Oh, it's wonderful, Miss Rossie!" I cried.

"Thank you, Veanie. I'm glad you know a great work of art when you see it. But don't you think I made the subject too handsome?"

They smiled at each other and at me. I had a feeling in me I hadn't had before, and for a minute it all but choked my throat. I didn't know why, not then. Much later I could understand: the white woman had taken me into her house; on that Sunday morning the white man and his wife, easily and naturally, had included me in their love for each other. I had a family feeling.

I hurried through my good breakfast of bacon and eggs and toast, and tidied up the kitchen. Then, without any hesitation, I went to Mrs. Lee in her bedroom and asked, "Miss Rossie, will you show me how to draw like you?"

She regarded me for a moment. "Honey," she said, "you've got to have a little talent, they say, before you can do it or even try to learn it. It isn't like playing a game or cutting from a pattern."

I felt too bad to ask her what was talent.

"Anyhow," she said, "I'll show you, when I have time."

Eagerly I said, "Can I practice by myself?"

"Yes. There's paper in the desk in the dining room and some pencils and colors in the drawer. But if I were you I wouldn't try to draw a person at first. Try an object, like this." She moved an empty vase to the center of her dressing table, rumpled a scarf around it, and sketched the setup, shading and all, in less than five minutes.

That evening, when Mr. and Mrs. Lee went out, I sat beside Edie's bed telling her a story. I could hardly wait. I thought she was never going to get to sleep.

"Edie, darling," I said, "let's pretend you're Snow White. A baby bear is going to come and find you in his bed. Now shut your eyes and play like you're sleeping till I get down to that part."

I went on with the story, talking slowly. Edie's eyes fluttered. "Hurry, Beanie," she murmered drowsily. "Bring the bear." In another moment she was fast asleep, and I turned off her light.

I ran to the broad mahogany desk and took out paper and pencils. I placed a pale green vase on top of the piano, rumpled the brocade scarf as Miss Rossie had done, and set to work. Soon the wastebasket was heaped with paper. I laid on the desk the sketch I thought my best and was trying to copy a picture from Edie's storybook when I heard Mr. and Mrs. Lee at the door. I ran to open it, holding my finished sketch.

"Look, Miss Rossie; I did it, just like you showed me!"

While Miss Rossie examined my picture I was so excited that I hopped from one foot to the other. Mr. Lee was hanging up his coat.

"Honey," Miss Rossie called to him. "Come and see what Veanie has done."

Mr. Lee joined her. "Why, that's good, Veanie," he said. "Do you take drawing at school?"

"No, sir; I just—"

"She's never tried it before, and I showed her only today," Miss Rossie said and I could hear the excitement in her voice.

"You sure have the knack, don't you!" said Mr. Lee.

"Knack." That must be the same thing as "talent." "Yes, ma'am—I mean, yes, sir; sure do," I said with solemn pride.

"All except your shadows," Miss Rossie said. "Wait a few minutes and I'll help you."

"Honey," said Mr. Lee, "you aren't going to start on that tonight, are you? It's pretty late."

"Oh, it won't take long, not for great artists like us. We're fast, aren't we, Veanie."

"Yessum." I laughed; I was bursting with happiness.

Mrs. Lee went into her bedroom and when she came back I showed her my second picture, the one I was still working on from Edie's story book. It was a scene out of Snow White.

"That's pretty, Veanie," Miss Rossie said. "But what's this space for?"

"Oh—that's for Snow White. You said don't try people first, Miss Rossie, so I'll put her in later on."

She asked to see the picture in the book. "That's an easy one, Veanie, because it shows her profile."

"What's profile, Miss Rossie?"

"When the side of a person's face is toward you—Get yourself a chair and sit here. I'll show you."

I placed the chair where she had pointed, near the desk lamp where the light was on my face. She sat at the desk, pencil poised. "Ready?"

"Yessum," I said eagerly, and bounced up straight and looked solemn.

She laughed. "No, keep smiling. You're cuter that way."

Quickly she completed her sketch. She held it up for me to see. "There! Does it look like you?"

"No, ma'am. But it's just like Mingie."

She began to laugh, and then I had to laugh too. We worked

late, Miss Rossie watching and correcting while I tried to copy my, or Mingie's, profile.

Mingie came by for me the next afternoon. The night before, I had hugged my secret to myself. Now I said, "Mingie, come see what I did. Miss Rossie showed me yesterday how to do it."

"Golly, Veanie. They're pretty!" Mingie sighed wistfully. "Mrs. Porter's real nice but I sure wish she could do all the things Miss Rossie does: draw, sew, embroider, play the piano—"

"Oh Mingie," I interrupted, "remember that new piece of music Mr. Lee brought back when he went to Tampa?"

"Yeah, you told me. Everybody's singing it—'Darkness on the Delta.'" She began to hum it.

"Well, I can play it," I said. "Last week when they went to Palm Beach and I came to clean up, I was practicing a long time."

Mingie laid down my drawings and began to close the windows. "Come on, Veanie, and play it. I know some of the words."

"But Mingie, they'll be home real soon. They just went out to the papaya grove."

"Well, play it soft-like, Veanie. Just once. Come on," she coaxed.

I played it more than once, of course. Mingie was singing soprano and I was singing alto. Mingie was swinging her arms and bumping her knees on the edge of the piano stool in time to the rhythm. My heels were bouncing on the rug and my shoulders swaying with each beat. In the middle of a verse Mingie broke off and I looked up to see her mouth snap shut. Mr. and Mrs. Lee had come in the back way from the garage and were standing there.

I met their eyes and my fingers slid from the keys. Mingie

looked as if she'd like to slide right under the piano and out of sight. I wished I could too.

"Why, that was good!" Miss Rossie exclaimed.

Mr. Lee asked, "Did you learn to play it by the notes, Veanie?"

"No, sir," I said. "I—I just heard you playing it."

"Do it again," he said, "and with the singing too."

We repeated our performance, but with less exuberance, of course. I slid off the stool and stood beside Mingie.

Mr. Lee took my place. His fingers moved over the keys, and he sang in his clear tenor. It was very different from the way I had played. It was beautiful.

"When I was a kid," Mr. Lee said, "my teacher blew his wig if I played a chord that wasn't written there. I had an ear, but he didn't let me use it."

He shook his head over that old teacher blowing his wig. Then he played the same piece in a different way. He rose and setttled himself in Miss Rossie's chair; she was perched on its arm. "Go on and try it again, Veanie," he urged.

I played it again, this time following as closely as I could the pattern of his performance.

"Well done," said Mr. Lee. He and Miss Rossie were holding hands.

When we were walking home, Mingie said, "Veanie, they weren't mad at us."

"No." I thought for a moment. "You know, Mingie," I said, "they don't ever get mad."

"Miss Rossie sometimes gives us her 'bad' look," Mingie reminded me.

I remembered our mama who had run away leaving us little more than her "green limbs" she had beat us with. And the way she used to scowl blackly at us, hands on hips. Mingie was thinking of her too. "No, that's not the same," she said.

"Not like Mama, or anybody. Miss Rossie never—*not ever*—!"

We stared at each other in awe.

Another evening, when Mingie and I were walking home together, one of Mrs. Lee's neighbors was coming down the street in our direction. Mingie stopped. "There's that old nosey," she said. "Bet she ask us a whole lot of questions."

"Yeah."

"If she does, don't say nothing."

When the woman reached us, Mingie was leaning against the truck of a palm tree with her arms over her head, elbows sticking out and her hands hugging the tree from behind. I was busy scribbling patterns in the smooth whitish spaces between the rings around the tree.

"Hello, Mingie and Veanie," the woman said pleasantly. "My, you two are growing! Which one is Mingie? No, don't tell me." She pointed. "You're Mingie. Mrs. Lee says you always were a little bit heavier. How old are you now?"

"We're 'leven."

"No, Veanie,' Mingie said. "Twelve."

"Twelve," I said.

"You've been with Mrs. Lee a long time, haven't you?"

"Yes, ma'am," Mingie answered, looking up into the tree.

"You two love her very much, don't you."

"Yes, ma'am." We answered that together.

"Does she still help Mr. Lee in the office sometimes?"

Mingie didn't answer. I started, "Ye—" Mingie gave me a look, and I didn't finish.

There was a silence. The woman looked at us and she wasn't so pleasant any more. "Well, tell Mrs. Lee hello for me." She went off, her heels clicking angrily.

We relaxed from our fixed positions and resumed our walk

home. "Veanie, said my sister, "you started to tell her. You know Miss Rossie said not to gossip, and people who ask so many questions are gossipers or else they wouldn't be that nosey."

"Did Miss Rossie say 'nosey'?"

"No, but that's what she meant."

"Aunt Tiller's nosey," I said.

"But that's for us. It ain't against us or against Miss Rossie."

The distinction wasn't hard. "Mingie, I wasn't gonna tell her nothing. I was just gonna say yessum. She's always asking me questions."

"You don't tell her, do you?"

"No—well, not always. Sometimes I go 'cross the street and don't meet her."

"That's right. Always don't say nothing. I don't even tell Mrs. Porter things. One day she said, 'Rossie sure does like you two little gals, doesn't she?' And I didn't answer yes, ma'am, and I didn't answer no, ma'am."

"What did she do?

"Nothing. She just laughed."

9

THE FIRST DAY of school in September, like all other school openings, was noisy with eager-faced young people full of curiosity about new teachers, new pupils, and the like. For Mingie and me it was a very special day, different from any other first day of school. The children from the first through the sixth grades had all been together in the same class, and by the sixth grade many had dropped out to go to work. But in the seventh grade there were separate classes for separate subjects, and many books to be bought. The seventh grade was, in fact, the beginning of high school.

Mingie and I stood in the line before the sales desk. Most of the others in the line were talking, joking, showing off their new clothes, and getting acquainted with newcomers. Mingie and I held our heads together and scanned the sheet of blue paper in Mingie's hand.

Mingie kept her voice low. "Veanie, we don't have enough money for all these books."

106

"How much are they all?"

"I haven't added them up yet. But look at this one—two-fifty all by itself. I've got four dollars. You?"

"Five."

"That's nine." She shook her head. "Tell you what we do, Veanie. Let's buy one set together."

"Yeah!" I was struck by Mingie's practical brilliance. But then I had a thought. "Suppose we're not in the same class at the same time?"

"We'll have to be. We'll sit together."

I nodded. But of course! We'd always sat together.

"Hand me the money then."

I untied the knots in the yellow-flowered handkerchief I held balled in my fist, smoothed out the bills, and gave them to Mingie.

Our turn came. The brisk woman behind the desk took Mingie's blue paper, the seventh-grade book list. We both waited anxiously. With her pen she swiftly summed up the prices. "That will be eight dollars and fifty cents."

Mingie flinched, sighed, and slowly counted out our wrinkled bills while the woman selected the books from the long shelf behind her and stacked them on the desk. Dividing them between us, we carried them away.

A bell rang. We were waiting at the door of the assembly room. The first to go in, we slid into one of the double seats. After everyone was seated a teacher made her entrance. She looked over the room, counted, and said: "The class—just as we thought—is too large and will be divided. I will have to send half of you down the hall to Room Five."

Mingie and I pushed close together in our seat.

"I don't like her," I whispered.

"Get ready," Mingie said. "We'll be the first out."

With an important look on her face the teacher said: "I think I shall do it this way—"

She stepped to the center of the room and gestured with her head and hand. "This double row will split down the middle. At the sound of the next bell everyone to the left will go to Room Five."

Mingie and I were in the center row. When the bell sounded we scrambled out of the seat and ran toward the door.

"Stop! One moment, please. You twins, come back and walk like young ladies. You're in high school now. Sit right where you were, then get up and march out as you should."

Most of the class was still seated. All eyes were on us. Reluctantly I returned to my seat and not until I reached it did I realize that if Mingie came back, too, the teacher would see at once that one of us had disobeyed her. Mingie had realized this before I did. Mingie remained standing right where she was.

The teacher looked at her. "I said go back and sit down." she commanded.

"Yes, ma'am; but—" Mingie started toward her.

"Young lady, sit down!"

The class roared with laughter as Mingie backed up and eased in beside me.

"I see now," the teacher said. "You were not to go out." She pointed to me. "But you were." She waited until the last snickers had subsided. "Now you may go, as you were instructed, please."

When recitations were over, Mingie and I met in the hall and consulted together. There was only one thing to do: tell Miss Rossie; she would fix it.

As I related to Miss Rossie what had happened, I became tearful. High school! I had not known how much I had looked forward to it. And now this! The teacher had been just plain mean. It wouldn't have meant anything to her, it wouldn't have hurt her, to let Mingie and me be together. And now we were in separate classes and we had only one set of books.

Miss Rossie said, "What did you and Mingie do, buy one set of books between you?"

"Yes, ma'am. And we want you to please, ma'am, call them up and tell them we have to study together."

Mrs. Lee's bright eyes were thoughtful. "Well," she said, "let's not get too excited about it, honey. It's not that bad. We'll figure out something."

Mingie came by in the afternoon. She immediately asked me: "Did you?"

"Yes."

Mrs. Lee heard our voices and came to us on the back porch. She said, "Mingie, you're a little early, aren't you?"

"Yes, ma'am. Mrs. Porter took the baby out with her. She said I could come on here."

"Yes. She called and asked me why you were sulky today. I told her I thought you were a little upset. But when things go wrong with you, Mingie, you shouldn't act that way around someone it doesn't concern. It doesn't help any and it's hard on the other person. Now about your books—"

"Yes, ma'am, Miss Rossie," Mingie said. "I'm sorry if I was ugly to Mrs. Porter."

"You weren't ugly, honey. She just said that you weren't as pleasant as usual. It's all right. I explained it to her."

Then Miss Rossie told us she would lend us the money for a second set of books. We would pay it back, fifty cents a week.

We thanked her politely. My disappointment was so great that I could have cried, but I was getting too big for crying now. I was in high school.

Miss Rossie looked from one of us to the other. "You know," she said, "they say so many things about twins. Maybe it's better for you not to be in the same classes. They say—I don't know—" Her voice trailed off.

It worried us to see Miss Rossie doubtful, she who had always seemed so sure about everything. Mingie and I hurried to reassure her. Why, it would be good for us, sure. It would be better. Why, what had happened this morning was the very best thing that could have happened.

We didn't talk about it ever again, Mingie and I. As we had, in time, accepted our separation in work, so we accepted our further separation in school.

Saturday was payday. Mrs. Lee came to the parlor where I was dusting. "Here's your money, Veanie."

'Thank you, ma'am." I put it into my apron pocket.

She waited, with a teasing sort of smile on her face. I straightened up. What she had given me hadn't felt like money. Puzzled, I looked at her. I said, "Miss Rossie, ma'am, did you think to take out the fifty cents for the books?"

"Well, I don't know," she said. "That's up to Mr. Lee. Suppose we look."

From my pocket I took out a piece of blue paper. I studied it and turned it round and round.

Miss Rossie stopped her teasing. "It's a check, Veanie. Five dollars. Mr. Lee feels you deserve a raise. You'll have five dollars every week from now on. And Veanie, it would be good for you to start a savings account at the bank. Just take the check there and they'll tell you how to do it."

Mingie came by for me that evening, and on our way home I felt bad because she hadn't got a raise too. "Maybe Mrs. Porter will give you more next time," I said. "Maybe Miss Rossie will tell her how much she gives me and that will make her want to pay you the same."

"Yeah." Mingie didn't believe Mrs. Porter would do that. Mingie scuffled a stone from the side of the road and kicked it. "Well," she said, "if she doesn't, maybe—I'll just sort of mention it to her."

"No, Mingie, you can't. Miss Rossie says don't be nasty, you know."

"Oh, I wasn't going to be nasty at all. I was just going to tell her smiling, or something like that."

"Oh—"

All through the morning of next payday Mingie tried to get up enough nerve to talk to Mrs. Porter about a raise. Each time she swallowed her words. She made queer gulping sounds whenever Mrs. Porter came near her.

At two o'clock when Mingie was getting ready to leave, Mrs. Porter laid a banknote on the kitchen cabinet. "Here's your money, Mingie," she said. "Two dollars more. Five dollars from now on."

Mingie couldn't even gasp out a thank you, ma'am. After all that gulping down of words she couldn't bring up anything at all. Mrs. Porter looked at her and laughed.

I had saved my first check and now had a second one. On Monday Mingie and I went to the bank and opened separate savings accounts.

Our lives were full—busy and orderly—and time passed swiftly with payday after payday. Edie was growing up and going to school. For a while I missed playing with her but I liked helping her with her lessons when she began to have homework.

At night Mingie and I were "going out." When we were smaller we used to hear from our porch, when the wind was in our direction, a shout of laughter or the sound of singing with a tinkle of music, and we'd steal down the road a piece to glimpse, through a window, the gaiety and lively movement of a party; and sometimes we'd overhear the voices of "grown-up young folks" in mysterious intimacy. Now we were ourselves becoming "grown-up young folks," going to a party in somebody's house or talking boy-and-girl talk on somebody's porch. There were soft warm nights when everything smelled so sweet and the moon seemed so near that we had to shout and sing clear up to the stars—and did—until from a window came the angry yell of some "old grownup" who had forgotten what it was like to be young.

At first Mingie and I told each other everything. We studied together, I with my books on my side of the table and Mingie with hers on the other, and it seemed silly to have had that extra expense of two sets of the same books, even though Mr. Lee had paid for the second set. But I liked to study more than Mingie did; and more and more we'd be reading different things, books or magazines we had borrowed or been given for Christmas presents or got by exchange with our friends. And little by little Mingie made friends who were not mine; and I had my own friends, too. Sometimes I'd be home alone; sometimes Mingie. When that happened, Aunt Tiller would hobble over, and when she went back to her own cabin, her light kept shining until the second one of us came home. I called her "nosey."

"Mingie," I asked, "why does she keep on watching us?"

"I guess to make sure we're not being bad. Miss Rossie wouldn't want us to be bad."

"But Mingie, we haven't got nothing to be bad about, have we?"

Mingie gave me a funny look. "N-no."

I felt uncomfortable and Mingie seemed embarrassed too, but she didn't say anything more, and somehow I couldn't say anything either.

A friend of mine told me that she had seen Mingie several

times down at the railroad waiting for the train to come in. "Looks like she's meeting somebody off that train."

I laughed at her though I was mad at her for spying and for thinking she knew something about my sister that I didn't know. "Why would she be meeting anybody off the train?"

My friend—but I no longer considered her a friend—gave me that same kind of funny look. "You know," she said, "Mingie's getting real pretty."

Vague worries came to live in my mind and I couldn't be rid of them. But how could I have any doubts about my twin? Why, that would be like trying to believe the world was flat, not round; or that the picture I was drawing of Mingie wasn't her at all but somebody I didn't know—a stranger!

I pushed away the fears.

I was happy, happier, it seemed to me, than I had ever been in my life. From my first term in high school, and maybe even earlier, I had known that I was going to be a teacher. I wanted to tell Mingie but I couldn't. It cost a lot of money just to be going to high school. It would cost more, much more, to go to college. Mingie would point that out right away, and suppose she laughed at me? Mingie didn't care about school the way I did. She was not falling behind, but she did not care for doing the extra work we did to get extra credit.

College. I must be crazy to have such a notion. All the same at night when I was in bed sometimes I would hear Miss Rossie's voice: "College—"

Anyhow, there was plenty of time. And so I didn't tell Mingie. I hugged my secret to myself.

I O

ONCE OR TWICE I had met Mingie's friend Sam. He was small and slight with smooth brown skin and very light brown eyes and he walked with a slight limp. He was much older than Mingie and me—about eleven or twelve years older— and he had a job as an expressman on the train. It was Sam that Mingie was meeting at the railroad.

For weeks everybody had been saying that Mingie and Sam meant to get married. For weeks I'd been telling myself they were wrong; it couldn't be. Mingie was too young, and she was so sensible. Sam had been married once before. Why, Sam was just about an old man!

One morning we were walking to school together. Mingie said: "Veanie, Sam and me—me and Sam—we're going to get married."

I didn't say anything.

"Aren't you glad?"

"Mingie, you can't!" I cried wildly.

114

"I can't?" She looked suddenly angry.

"Why, why? You're still going to school—" I stammered.

"Oh, that!" Mingie laughed. She was laughing at me.

I sat through one class and then I ran to Mrs. Lee's. She wasn't home. I let myself in and waited for her. When I heard her footsteps, I was at the door. "Oh, Miss Rossie, Miss Rossie, she's going to get married!" I choked over the words.

Miss Rossie walked by me and laid down the packages she had in her arms. Without looking back at me, she began to open the brown bags. She said quietly, "Yes. Go on, honey. Tell me. I'm listening."

"It's Mingie, Miss Rossie." I begged her: "Don't let her get married, Miss Rossie. Please don't let her." The tears were streaming down my face.

Miss Rossie finished putting away her groceries and then sat down in a chair. "Now, Veanie, there's no need to cry over that. I know all about it. She told me."

I thought I hadn't heard. I couldn't have heard. Mingie had told Miss Rossie, and it was all right? I couldn't see because my tears were blinding me, so maybe I hadn't heard either.

"Yes, and I—I told her—"

Miss Rossie hestitated. I waited, listening hard, trying to stop my sobs.

"I asked her if she was certain. We talked a long time, Veanie. After an hour I knew that Mingie was sure. She'll be happy, Veanie."

"But you don't understand. She'll leave me! Don't let her leave me! She'll listen to you. Please ma'am, Miss Rossie."

"Veanie, I don't think I should interfere. Honey, you're the one who doesn't understand. Mingie's in love, and she has a nice young man. She wants to marry and have a family of her own. Why should I try to stop her? It wouldn't be right. Some-

115

times a great mistake is made by keeping a girl from marrying when she wants to."

I wasn't crying aloud any more, but the tears kept welling into my eyes, and I had to brush them away.

"But Miss Rossie, Mingie's not quite fifteen yet, and I want her to finish high school with me, and then—"

"Yes, I know. I reminded Mingie of school, but she knows what she wants. Veanie, suppose it was you who wanted to marry. How would you like it if I said No?"

"I don't want to; not till after I graduate. And Mingie shouldn't. Please, Miss Rossie."

"Veanie, you and Mingie are twins, but in some ways Mingie is older than you. She's bigger, fuller. She's a woman. Men often take advantage of girls who are alone, but if you have a husband, you have protection. I'd rather see both of you get married early than—than ruin your lives by getting into trouble." She rose. "Stop weeping and moaning as if Mingie—was dead or something. You'd have to do without her some day anyhow."

I could see that she herself was upset, and I persisted. "Yes, ma'am, but—but—"

"No, 'buts' about it, honey. Mingie is sure she wants to marry so we must think of her and hope she'll be happy. She'll be all right."

"Yes, ma'am." I was wiping my face.

"Now you're being a sensible girl and a loving sister." Miss Rossie reached out and drew me to her. "Try not to worry, Veanie. I know you'll miss her. I will, too. And don't forget that she's going to miss us. You can go up and help her with her house on week ends and holidays."

"Go up? Where?" I gasped with alarm. "Where?"

"Up to Lakeland. Didn't you know she's moving to Lakeland with Sam?"

116

"Oh no, ma'am, Miss Rossie. She didn't tell me that. She didn't tell me she was going away. No! No!" My voice rose hysterically. "Mingie's leaving me, she's leaving me!"

I slumped to the floor.

When I came to my senses, I was on the sofa. I heard Miss Rossie, and for the first time her voice was stern, not soft and gentle. "Veanie! Veanie! You stop this! You're acting like a spoiled child."

My eyes rose to a dear face that was flushed and hurt-looking. She had done so much; she was doing all she could to make things better for Mingie and for me. And I was hurting her!

I felt the tight grip on my arms relax and tenderness return. "Miss Rossie," I said weakly, "I'm so sorry. I didn't mean to act that way."

"Come on, now." Her voice was gentle again. "Let's wash your face in cold water. Just look how you're perspiring. You can't let Mingie see you looking like that when she comes by for you this evening."

That evening I waited as usual, but Mingie never came by for me. It was nearly dark when I started for home and as I walked along the night pressed down on me like a heavy weight. Perhaps I was appreciating fully, for the first time, how many of the decisions that had had to be made had fallen on Mingie.

I was near the tracks now. I walked slowly between the tall bushes on the dirt road. A big round stone in the path reminded me of the night of the lynching. What would I have done that night without Mingie?

At the cabin I saw that the padlock on the door was as we'd left it in the morning. So Mingie wasn't home yet. I couldn't go in. It would be so lonely inside. I sat on the steps and waited.

This was the way it was going to be. Always. No more Mingie and me. Just me.

At last I picked up the key out of the flower can where we kept it; Mingie had made that decision, too. I unlocked the door. I struck a match and lit the kerosene lamp on the table. Some time later I found myself still standing in the center of our front room holding the kerosene lamp in both hands. It was so still. Only a little gray mouse moved, and he made no sound at all.

I carried the lamp into the back room, set it on the low table beside the bed, and turned the wick dim. I kicked off my shoes. Without taking off my clothes, I crawled into bed and pulled the covers over my head.

It was very late when I heard Mingie's sandals scuff on the porch, accompanied by heavier footsteps. I tucked the blanket tightly about my face and tried to make myself relax; I was trembling. I heard hushed talking on the porch. It stopped. On tiptoe Mingie came to the bed. I felt her ease in behind me. After a moment she leaned over, pulled off the blanket, and kissed my hot cheek.

I never moved. I just lay there, rigid. Mingie's arm was around me and I was afraid she'd feel how I was quivering inside. My muscles were tired and strained.

How many questions I wanted to ask Mingie! But I couldn't, not now. And Miss Rossie had said not to bother Mingie, not to worry her. I would wait until morning. It would be better then. In the morning maybe Mingie all by herself would tell me everything I wanted to know. Then it would be all right. We would talk and talk. Everything would be all right in the morning.

I fell asleep.

When I woke, it was early. Mingie was not in bed beside me, and the house was silent. I sat up. Under heavy lids I looked about the room. Its stillness was ghostlike. My feet dragged on the floor. I went hopelessly to the closet. Years ago—long, long ago it seemed now—Miss Rossie had showed us how to make a closet, how to hammer in two boards so that they stuck out into the room and hang curtains on the three sides. Mingie had done most of it. She had made the curtains.

I opened the curtains. Instead of pairs of identical dresses on the hooks, there was now only one of each. Three pairs of shoes sat on the shelf; the matching three pairs were gone. I saw now that Mingie's toilet articles had disappeared; only mine were on the bureau.

I felt a sudden rush of fear. It was like the time Mingie and I had come home and found the house strange and empty; Mama was gone.

I went to the chest and pulled out the three long drawers. Everything of Mingie's had been taken away. But in the bottom drawer still lay the two shut-eye dolls Miss Rossie had given us four or five years ago. They lay asleep in the little quilted sacks Miss Rossie had taken so much pains with, one pink and one blue. They had been our very first dolls. Mingie had left them side by side. They would never leave each other.

I took up the dolls and cuddled them, remembering that happy Christmas morning Mingie and I had leaped with joy at the sight of the babylike pink legs and big round heads. Hugging them tight in my arms, I threw myself sobbing across the bed. "Mingie! Oh, Mingie! Miss Rossie, Miss Rossie, you let her go away!"

My emotions exhausted me, and I fell asleep. The sound of gunfire wakened me. I lay very still, listening to the beat of my heart. Only one heart now; that other time there were two—Mingie's and mine, as we clung together under the house. This time I wouldn't hide. I didn't care. Let them come.

Music. Music in a lynching? I realized it was Armistice day, the people were celebrating. I looked at the clock. Eleven o'clock—November 11—the first day in my life without Mingie.

A horn sounded two short toots—Miss Rossie's signal. I had forgotten. Miss Rossie had expected me early today. Mr. Lee was taking part in the ceremonies downtown, and she had wanted to go with him.

Footsteps mounted to the porch. "Veanie?"

Miss Rossie opened the door and came in. "Veanie?" Then she saw me and hurried to the bed. "Veanie, honey, are you sick?" She sat down, put a hand on my shoulder, and pulled me over. "What's the matter, Veanie?"

She looked about the room. She got up and went to the closet and pushed aside the curtains as I had done. She came back to the bed. "Mingie is already gone?"

At last I could speak. "Yes, ma'am," I said dully.

"I thought—tomorrow."

Edie had followed her mother from the car. When she saw my soaked, bloated face she put a hand on my forehead. "Oh, mother, she's real hot," Edie said. "Veanie's got a fever."

I reached up and took the small fingers in my own. Miss Rossie touched my face. "Yes, you are hot, honey," she said, but she knew I had no fever. She sighed. "Veanie, there's no sense in this at all! Have you had your breakfast?"

"No, ma'am. I don't want any."

"But, Veanie, you got to," said Edie importantly. "You won't grow up to be a nice big girl if you don't eat." She was talking as I had often talked to her. She was being Veanie to little Edie, and she did it so perfectly that I had to smile.

Miss Rossie hugged us both, one arm for her little girl beside her, the other for her second little girl, the dark one, in the bed. "Come on now and get up, Veanie. You and Edie will go with us. You can walk and play in the park while we're in the auditorium. Hurry. We haven't much time, and I need you."

Quickly I rose, washed, and changed my dress. Hurry. Miss Rossie and Edie need you. Hurry.

I I

FOR MONTHS after Mingie's going my world was dark and dreary. Friends began to fall away. At school it was hard for me to stand up before the class when I was called on. I stammered and stuttered, or my mind went blank, and I found myself standing there with the class snickering and the teacher frowning. My classmates said gleefully that Mingie had run away with our single brain, the one we'd shared between us. These were the envious ones who had resented our good luck, and I knew that. It hurt, all the same. I began to miss classes. Some days I didn't go to school at all.

On one of those days, the worst of them, I was like a trapped animal in my pain. My thoughts went round and round. . . . If I had gone to Mrs. Vann's or Mrs. Porter's instead of Mingie, everything would have been different. Mingie wouldn't have left Miss Rossie. Or would she? I remembered how she had been growing in the last year, filling out under my eyes;

everyone had seen it but me. I remembered it had been a long time since anyone had not been able to tell us apart. Mingie, a woman at fifteen! It wasn't right; we were twins. She'd had no right to grow like that, to grow away from me. How could Mingie want to get married when I didn't want to? And why hadn't she told me sooner? We would have talked about it, and I'd have told her that we'd go to college together and then she would have changed her mind and not married Sam. But why hadn't I told her? Hadn't I been thinking about going to college alone, without Mingie? Was that why I hadn't told her? But I wouldn't have run away from Mingie. Why had she run away from me? Miss Rossie could have stopped her. Miss Rossie was against me; she was on Mingie's side. . . .

I heard the two toots of a horn and gave a start of alarm. I had forgotten. I had forgotten to go to Mrs. Lee's!

But I didn't run out to meet her. Miss Rossie found me lying on the small couch where I had been all morning holding a sketch of Mingie in my hand.

"Veanie, why didn't you come? I was waiting for you."

She glanced around the disordered room. "Have you been to school today?"

"No, ma'am."

"Why not?"

I had no answer.

She became stern. "Veanie, your marks aren't half as good as they used to be. You're staying home without reason, and against all reason. I've wanted so much for you to have a good education, and now—look at you! You're just moping!"

She took the picture out of my hand.

"That's the first drawing you made of Mingie," I said. "When we were about ten."

123

"Yes, and it's good, and look at the way you've bent it!" Miss Rossie the artist was indignant.

Veanie, the lesser artist, knew just how she felt. "Oh, Miss Rossie, I'm so sorry."

"Veanie, get up. Get up and do something. Don't just sit there."

"Miss Rossie, they laugh at me in school. They say Mingie ran away."

"And that's why you're not going to school? Veanie, I'm ashamed of you. You know very well that Mingie didn't run away. She left the way she did because she was afraid of how you'd carry on and she didn't know if she could stand that. She loved Sam and she loved you, too. It was very hard for her. In the last letter I got from her she asked about you in a way that told me she worries."

I felt a bitter satisfaction. So Mingie was worrying about me. Good! Let her just keep on worrying. Let her worry herself sick.

Miss Rossie went on: "You said once that your papa told you and Mingie that the last thing your mother said—your real mother—was, 'God, please bless my babies.' Well, He has blessed both of you, Veanie, hasn't He?"

"Yes, ma'am."

"Then never mind what they say at school. You've got something more important to do than to listen to them."

She looked at my set face. A little line appeared between her eyes. "Oh, Veanie, I don't know what to do for you—I just don't know—!"

And suddenly I seemed to have waked from a bad dream. I saw the room with my clothes strewn about and the sand dust covering everything and I was ashamed. I saw and was ashamed of more than just that. I knew the mean and ugly bitterness that had been raging in me. I saw Miss Rossie's patience with me during all these months. Yes, I had been moping. I hadn't been thinking about Mingie or about Miss Rossie. I had been feeling mighty sorry for—myself!

My remorse and my rush of love for Miss Rossie and Mingie were so great that they made me dizzy. The room spun round.

"Veanie, are you all right?"

I let out a deep breath. I felt the floor under me. I was on my feet. "I'm all right, Miss Rossie, ma'am. I—I'm fine."

She looked at me, and the line between her eyes went away. "Can I expect you tomorrow, Veanie?"

"Oh, yes, Miss Rossie; I'll be there, right after school."

She smiled and went to the door. "I must go for Edie now."

I followed her to the porch. "My, but your flowers are growing pretty," she said. She touched one and turned its face up and smiled down at it. "Look how lovely it is!" she said, and suddenly the flower I had looked at and passed by a hundred times came into full being; I looked, and it was lovely. She had that way—not always but often—of making the world shine wherever you were, when she came into it.

She waved at me from her car as she drove off. I hurried in. I looked at myself in the mirror and called myself names and then I felt much better. I cleaned the cabin and myself and settled down to my books.

At the end of the term my report card was much better; my average stood next to the highest in the class. Proudly I showed it to Miss Rossie.

"Veanie, this is just grand! I knew it. I knew you could do it!"

Edie ran and brought her own report card. "Look at mine,

Veanie. My teacher says I'm good; didn't she, mother? She pointed. "See? It says so right here. We're smart, aren't we, Veanie?"

"That's right, Edie, honey," I said. "And we're going to be even smarter."

The little girl looked at me with great round blue eyes. "Veanie—are we? Really?"

"Yes, we are," I said.

Miss Rossie laughed happily.

When I was ready to go home that evening, Miss Rossie came to the kitchen. "Veanie, how would you like to go up and see Mingie next week end?"

I was taken by surprise and couldn't say a word. Then came a surge of joy. To see Mingie—why, there was nothing in the world I wanted so much! "Oh, yes, ma'am, Miss Rossie!"

She studied me for a moment. "Veanie—you know—it's going to be Aunt Veanie soon."

"Aunt—?"

"Didn't Mingie tell you? She's going to have a baby."

No, Mingie hadn't told me. We had been writing to each other, short little notes. Mingie hadn't told me; but she had told Miss Rossie.

Miss Rossie said hurriedly, "Isn't that wonderful, Veanie? Mingie's baby. It will be just like your own. I suppose she didn't tell you because she was afraid you'd be worried about her."

I knew that wasn't the reason. Up there, more than a hundred miles north, Mingie was feeling bad about the way she had left me. But the sudden bitterness died away. Mingie was going to have a baby. Oh, Mingie, honey—!

Many years ago when Mingie and I were very little, we had gone on a train with our mama. It had been so exciting, but there was Mama's angry voice, and slaps. Now it was even more exciting, and there couldn't be any slaps. I sat like a calm and composed young lady while the world slid by the windows, but inside me I was just like that little girl who had bounced up and down in her seat. Mingie! We would fall into each other's arms and hug and kiss, and maybe cry a little bit, and then we would talk and we would never, never stop.

Lakeland. I looked for Mingie at the station but I hadn't known what train I'd be coming on, so of course she wasn't there. Lakeland's colored town wasn't far from the station. The taxi stopped before a white-painted frame house with a shingled red roof. It had a long porch with a swing on it. Mingie had heard the taxi, and as I came up the steps the door opened.

We didn't fall into each other's arms. We didn't kiss and hug. We just stood there, staring at each other.

I was wearing a short dress, socks, and sandals. Mingie was wearing a grown-up dress, stockings, and high-heeled pumps. I was a schoolgirl; Mingie was a woman. We had dressed the same for so long. In the six months since I had seen her, she had never changed in my mind. And Mingie—what had she expected? I didn't know, but it couldn't have been this schoolgirl standing before her like her own ghost from another time and place.

And at the same time, standing there looking into my twin's eyes, I knew something was wrong that didn't have anything to do with me. And Mingie knew that I knew and was afraid.

On Sunday evening I was on the train again, going home. I had spent two strange days with Mingie. We had talked, in little spurts with odd silences in between. I had admired her nice four-room house and all the pretty things she had made: the ruffled curtains, the lace-edged doilies, the embroidered pillowcases. And how clean she kept everything! Why, you could eat off the floor, it was so clean. But Mingie didn't have a rug in the living room, and I knew she must have wanted one. And she didn't have a sewing machine; she had sewn everything by hand. I hadn't said a word about rug or sewing machine. Sam made good money, but after all you couldn't furnish a whole house with everything in just six months. Anyhow it wasn't any of my business; I mustn't be nosey.

I had helped Mingie with the housework, and we talked about Miss Rossie. And every time we got worried by one of our silences, Mingie had started up with, "Miss Rossie—" She was missing her so. She hadn't been able to keep that from me, it had kept slipping out.

On Sunday, Mingie had dressed like me in one of the short dresses she had gone away with and socks and sandals. And we had talked more and even laughed a little. But she had changed her outfit when Sam came home. Sam hadn't seemed pleased to see me, but he hadn't seemed happy to see Mingie either. With Sam there, Mingie had tried to act gay, and that had almost broken my heart.

All the time I was there, Mingie and I had been saying the important things without any words. We had been like two people stricken dumb who watch each other hard and give question and answer with their eyes. We knew each other that well.

Something was wrong, terribly wrong.

But Mingie was entirely happy about the baby, and that was what I told Mrs. Lee when I returned. "Miss Rossie, the baby is coming in October and Mingie hopes it will be a girl. She said to tell you that as soon as it's old enough she's going to bring it to see us."

"I can hardly wait to see Mingie nursing a baby," Miss Rossie said. "Veanie, how does she look? Is she all right?"

I didn't answer that. I said, "The baby doesn't show yet. Oh, Miss Rossie, I hope it will be twins!"

"I'll bet Mingie doesn't," Miss Rossie said, laughing.

She glanced at me. "How did you like Mingie's husband, Veanie?"

"I—I like him all right," I said.

I 2

IT WASN'T TWINS and it wasn't a girl. Mingie's baby was a boy and he was christened Timothy.

I could hardly have been happier when I met Mingie at the station, and she let me take little Timmy. They'd come alone, just Mingie and her baby. Miss Rossie was waiting for us at her house, so we went there right away. She met us on the porch, and her arms went out for the chubby child. "Oh, Mingie, he's so beautiful! Oh, please, Veanie, let me have him; you look to be smothering him."

Lovingly carrying the baby, she led us into the parlor. She laid Timmy on the big couch and laughed to see how tiny he looked there. She took him up again and cuddled him. "Mingie, you'll have to stay right here until Mr. Lee comes so he can see this baby."

"Yes, ma'am, Miss Rossie."

Miss Rossie gave her a quick searching look. Mingie was so thin. "It's so good to see you, Mingie. Sit down, honey. It must have been tiring, having to take care of him on the train."

"No, ma'am. I didn't get tired. He's real good and didn't cry at all."

Mingie sat in the big armchair, and I leaned against it with one arm around Mingie's shoulder. As one mother to another Miss Rossie asked Mingie about her pregnancy and labor. Mingie had had the baby at home and she had had to continue the housework very soon after. She had not been able to fully regain her strength.

Miss Rossie made baby sounds over Timmy, rocking him in her arms. "Oh, won't Edie be surprised when she wakes up! I didn't tell her you were coming today, Mingie. I just said I had a surprise for her if she'd take her nap early. You didn't tell her, did you, Veanie?"

"No, ma'am, but she's real smart. She said she had a secret for me about Mingie and she couldn't tell me till she woke up."

We heard Mr. Lee on the porch. "Honey, come in here and see Mingie's little boy," Miss Rossie called. "He's the prettiest thing!"

Her voice sounded as if she wasn't quite sure how her husband would take this visit.

Mr. Lee immediately let us all know by the way his face lit up when he saw his wife with the dark baby in her arms. "Well, if it isn't little old lady Mingie and her baby!" he teased as he shook Mingie's hand. He turned. "Come here, boy; let's have a look at you." He took the baby and sat on the couch with Timmy perched on one knee. "Cutest little boy I ever did see. How old is he now, Mingie? And where's his hair?

"He's four months old, Mr. Lee," Mingie said, laughing, "and I'm glad he doesn't have any hair."

"Mingie, he's fat as a pig. What do you feed him—raw beef?" He made chuckling sounds at Timmy and began to bounce him.

"No, sir," Mingie said happily. "I nurse him, and I've given him a few cans of baby food like Edie used to eat."

Little Timmy began to squirm. And then, before our eyes, a dark stream flowed down the leg of Mr. Lee's freshly pressed trousers. Startled, Mr. Lee hoisted the child. Timmy let out a wail. Mr. Lee looked suddenly frightened. "Oh, did I scare you, boy?" he said to Timmy, just as if he expected Timmy to answer.

I hurried to take the baby. Mingie seemed frozen in her horror, and Miss Rossie wasn't moving. Then we all realized that Miss Rossie was laughing. "Oh, dear," she wiped her eyes. "Oh, honey," she said to her husband, "if you could only see yourself! It's been so long that we've almost forgotten. Maybe it's time we had another one."

We were all laughing together when Mr. Lee retreated to the bedroom.

Mingie took Timmy from me. "I'll nurse him," she said, "and maybe he'll go to sleep."

"Better dry him before you feed him, Mingie," Miss Rossie said. "Leaving him wet is likely to irritate his skin."

"I know, ma'am, but he used up all his diapers on the train, Miss Rossie. I'll have to wait till I get home with Veanie and rinse some out."

"I've kept some of Edie's in the chest. I don't know why— maybe I was waiting all this time for Timmy. You can have them, honey. Let me change him now." Gathering up the baby, she went into the bedroom just as Mr. Lee was coming out, having changed his clothes.

"You bad little boy," he said, tapping the short, plump leg on Mrs. Lee's arm. Then he turned to us. "Mingie, did Veanie tell you about all the prizes she's been winning at school and at the fair?"

"Yes, sir. She sent me the ribbons to keep for her," Mingie said, with the first undertone of sadness in her voice.

"And I sent her half of the money, too," I added. Right away, I knew I shouldn't have said that.

"You'd better keep your money," Mr. Lee said. "Mingie has an old man now to look after her. How about that, Mingie?" he asked in his teasing way.

"Yes—yes, sir." And now Mr. Lee saw she was embarrassed.

Miss Rossie came back with Timmy and all innocently she too brought up the subject of my prizes. "Veanie, how much was it you won at the fair? Did you tell Mingie?"

"Yes, ma'am."

"For embroidery work, drawing, and basket making. How much was it?"

"Eighteen dollars."

"And that wasn't all!" Miss Rossie said. She thought I was being shy.

"You walked off with first in the Elks oratorical contest, didn't you, Veanie?" Mr. Lee put in. "How much was that?"

"Yes, sir. A ten-dollar gold piece."

Desperately I tried to change the subject. "Mingie, did you like the jelly I sent you?"

"It was real good, Veanie," Mingie said miserably.

"Veanie got a second prize for that jelly," said Miss Rossie proudly.

When Mr. Lee went back to his office, Miss Rossie led us into the bedroom and pulled open the bottom drawer of the chest. First she took out a little blue sweater suit she had made for Timmy, and while Mingie and I were exclaiming over it, she came to the bed where we were measuring the suit against Timmy, who was sleeping. She had a pile of pink, blue, and white baby clothes. "He's very big, but these are one-year-olds —so I think they'll be all right. . . . Oh, he's awake."

I confessed: "I woke him up so we could dress him."

Mrs. Lee playfully spanked me and said to Mingie, "He's such a fine little boy. How much does he weigh?"

"I don't know, ma'am. He was bigger but he fell off. The doctor said he has asthma."

"Is he taking anything for it?"

"I rub him every night with some salve."

"Salve the doctor gave you?"

"No, ma'am. Just some salve I had."

"Did the doctor say it was all right?"

"He doesn't know." Mingie was uncomfortable. "I just took the baby to the doctor one time."

"Well, it's best for the doctor to treat him. Why didn't you take him back? What does your husband think about it?"

Mingie looked at me as if for help, but I didn't know how to help her about this. "He—Sam said the—the baby is all right and doesn't need a doctor."

"Oh." Miss Rossie busied herself dressing little Timmy in the blue sweater suit. Then she said, "Mingie, asthma can be dangerous for a baby. When your husband gives you money, you just take part of it and have the doctor treat your little boy."

"Yes, ma'am. I was going to do that when Veanie sent me the twelve dollars, but—" She was floundering.

"Why didn't you, Mingie?"

"Well, I used it to buy him the little suit to come here in and some baby food the doctor said he had to have."

"Mother!" Edie was calling from her room.

Miss Rossie motioned us to come with her. Edie was sitting up in her bed, her face still flushed from her nap. Her eyes flew

134

wide open as Mingie placed Timmy on the bed beside her. "Oh! Oh!" She reached out.

"Be careful, Edie," Miss Rossie cautioned. "He can't sit alone yet."

"Look at him, Mother. Look at him! He looks like he's swimming!" She burst into delighted laughter.

"Edie, honey, you haven't said hello to Mingie."

Edie leaped out of bed and flung herself into Mingie's arms. "Why did you go away? I didn't want you to go away."

Later, when Miss Rossie drove us to the cabin, we were silent. I lingered behind when Mingie, carrying Timmy, walked up the path to our old house.

"Did you forget something, Veanie?" Miss Rossie asked.

"Oh—no, ma'am—" I didn't know how to say it; how could I ask Miss Rossie to help Mingie when she had already done so much?

There was a little frown on her face as she looked at me. Then, instead of speaking to me, she called to my sister: "Mingie, bring Timmy down tomorrow. About ten o'clock. I'd like to have Edie's doctor look him over."

"Oh, yes, ma'am! Thank you!" From the relief in Mingie's voice, we knew how worried she was about Timmy.

So began Mrs. Lee's care for Mingie's child. But Mingie's other worry was not one Mrs. Lee could solve. That trouble, though never mentioned by Mingie, became plainer and plainer to me.

I often wondered, in the ten days Mingie stayed with me, whether Mrs. Lee came to believe she had made a mistake in allowing Mingie to marry. Yet "allow" was not the way to think of it. Mrs. Lee had done no more than favor marriage over an alternative to which—as she knew—many young people resorted. Mingie and Sam wanted—and so Mrs. Lee favored for them—the respectable and right thing. Mingie had been too young and she had not given Mrs. Lee any opportunity to meet and know Sam. Mingie had been impatient and determined. And if the marriage wasn't working out as well as had been hoped, the fault wasn't Mrs. Lee's.

Yet, having favored the marriage, Mrs. Lee was the more concerned to help it succeed.

One thing Mingie never lacked was courage. With it now came a pride that to me was heartbreaking.

Timmy's treatments were well under way, and Mingie had been instructed in what to do for him when she was getting ready to leave. We were in the room we had shared for so long. I sat on the bed behind her while she combed her hair. Our eyes met in the mirror and mine fell away. They went down to her sleazy dress, laddered stockings, and down-at-the-heels shoes; then to the three flimsy dresses in the battered brown suitcase; and on the bed, the mended panties and one cheap pink slip. My eyes rose and again I was looking at my own— at Mingie's—in the mirror.

Miss Rossie had told me not to interfere but I couldn't help myself. I had to ask my twin the direct question: "Mingie, is— is Sam nice to you?"

"Why, yes, Veanie. He's nice. Why?" A blank smile spread over her thin face. I faltered.

"Oh, nothing. I just thought—"

"He says he's going to buy me a—ah—a nice outfit for Christmas, Veanie; a real pretty one. And I want you to get one just like it for when you come to see me."

She was pretending, so I had to pretend, too. "I'll do that!" I said with false enthusiasm. "Ah—what kind will it be— what color?"

"I think, something green—a suit with a flared or pleated skirt."

"I'll wait till I get there and buy mine, so they'll match."

At the station I climbed into the dusty coach behind my sister, Timmy kicking in her arms. I took him while she adjusted the big box lunch and special baby food which Mrs. Lee had given her. Then I laid Timmy on Mingie's lap, kissed them both, and turned away.

"Don't go yet, Veanie," Mingie called after me. "It's minutes before the train goes."

I said without looking back: "I thought I heard the conductor. I'll just go and see."

I climbed down to the platform where I had to wipe my eyes before showing myself to Mingie under her window.

How I wished for the train to start!

"A-a-ll aboard!" The shout came at last.

Mingie held up Timmy and waved his tiny hand. "Say bye-bye to your auntie, honey." She began brightly but her voice choked.

The engine puffed; the coach rattled.

"Write as soon as you get h—there," I called, avoiding the word *home*. I wouldn't think of Mingie's home as in Lakeland; it was with me.

"I will!"

I waved with my arm high before my face so that Mingie might not see the tears running down my face. The train was gone and I was still waving. I was crying without restraint and, as I left the station, I hoped I wouldn't meet anyone I knew.

I didn't have that luck. Near the station I happened upon two girls from school who were the last creatures I cared to meet on that day, or on any day. They were old enemies. In the days before we had found Miss Rossie, they were two who had laughed at Mingie and me. They always wore pretty clothes and they could well afford to; their fathers worked at the packing house where Mingie and I used to go to beg for cull oranges, grapefruit, and tangerines.

Now I looked just as well dressed as they did, better. I was wearing a plaid skirt Miss Rossie had given me and which I had altered in my home economics class; its matching blouse had belonged to one of Miss Rossie's friends. My black pumps were a pair Miss Rossie had bought for herself but they had hurt her feet. My socks, red, like the plaid in my skirt, were brand new.

"Yah, yah! Think you're hot 'cause the white folks give you their clothes!"

"Hey, Veanie, say something. Think you talk just like that white woman, don't you?"

"You and Mingie! Mingie had a baby and had to run off and get married. Yah, yah!"

My fingernails gouged into my palms. I wanted to pull those long braids out by the roots and strangle them with them.

"You're scared, dirty foot. You're not so hot to fight since Mingie ran off."

That almost did it. I was alone but in my fury I could have beaten up both of them. I could have—I could have killed them!

But I went on. I was a big girl now with a married sister and a nephew. I had a family that needed me. And I had Miss Rossie, who trusted me. Oh, God, make me be like Miss Rossie—patient and wise. These were children; they were as old as I was but they were children.

Children. All the same, the tongues of ugly gossip had lashed me. I was sick inside. I couldn't help thinking how strange it was that Mingie and I couldn't accept the help and kindness of Miss Rossie without being criticized by some of the white people, and Mingie and I couldn't accept her help without being attacked by some of our color.

Miss Rossie had given me the day off, but I found my feet leading me back to her, as always when I was in trouble. When I got to the house, it was closed. Nobody was home. I waited in the garden, yanking out a weed here and there as if they were the slander I was digging up by the roots—killing.

But how beautiful the place was. The lovely house among the white-trunked royal palms sheltering, in their majesty, the thick clusters of sweet-faced pansies. The newly mown lawn. The blooming bushes of pink double hibiscus. The dwarf-stemmed rose oleander lining the walk that led to the four wide steps, on each side of which sprang a tree vine of purple bougainvillia, accenting the green of the shutters and the rose of the gladioli under the windows. And within—the cool, faintly scented rooms I knew so well, filled with the presence of Miss Rossie. This was the dwelling place of love. . . .

I didn't hear Mr. Lee's car until the wheels were crackling on the white shells in the driveway. Edie in a blue bathing suit and rubber cap climbed down.

"Veanie!" she said in happy surprise. "You came to see me. I can swim real good now." She was tugging at her shoes. "Veanie, take my straps loose, please."

"Stand up then, honey," I told her. "You're just pulling them tight."

Her plump shoulders rose and she looked at me. "Have you been crying, Veanie?"

Mr. and Mrs. Lee had been taking things out of the car. Now they joined us. Mr. Lee was asking: "Isn't this a day off for Veanie, Rossie?"

"Yes. Mingie and the baby were supposed to leave this afternoon," she replied. Then she had a good look at me. "Veanie, what's wrong? Did Mingie get off all right?"

"Yes, ma'am. She's gone."

"Is that why you're crying?"

"No—no, ma'am—" I glanced at Mr. Lee. He cast a silent question at his wife and went into the house.

"Come to the bedroom," Miss Rossie said, and I followed her. She closed the door and sat on the bed. "All right, Veanie. What is it?"

I told her of the two girls who had said Mingie had had to run away because she was going to have a baby.

Miss Rossie interrupted with: "Why, Veanie, that's a lie and you know it is!"

"I do know it, Miss Rossie," I said, "because I counted it up, and it was eleven months before Timmy came."

Miss Rossie looked at me in a way that troubled me. And then I knew what the look meant, or maybe I had been ashamed of myself deep inside all the time. Why should I have had to count the months? Why should there be any doubts? Didn't I trust Mingie? And even if it hadn't been eleven months, if it had been less than nine—would that have mattered so much? I would love Mingie just the same.

Still I heard the taunting voices of my old enemies, and my pain and anger came out: "They tried to shame me for wearing your clothes and for trying to talk like you."

For a long time Miss Rossie was silent. Maybe she was thinking of her own trials with our bringing her our every trouble; there must be many things I didn't know anything about.

"Veanie," she said at last, "we can't stop them. What they say can't hurt you—unless you let it. The way won't be easy for Mingie and you. But then, it never is, not for anybody. You want your way made easy, that's only human. But when it is, when you no longer have troubles, what's really happened is that you've stopped growing, you've stopped trying. And to stop trying is a little like dying. It even *is* dying a little, Veanie."

13

I APPLIED MYSELF to my work at school. My grades steadily improved. My days brightened and Miss Rossie went about smiling, her step light, walking with her gay little bounce. It was sobering to realize that my welfare and my conduct were of such concern to her that they affected her happiness. I began to wonder about her, to see her as a person instead of just "my" Miss Rossie.

The overriding factor throughout the South is, of course, its Negro population. Everywhere the prime problem is what to do for the Negro: to help him or to hinder him, to accept him or just to use him. The "solutions" are almost as many as there are people and they range from doing nothing to attempting everything at once.

The Negro, someone has said, is on the conscience of every sensitive Southerner. Our Miss Rossie—Mrs. Lee—was a Southerner and sensitive in the highest meaning of the word. It was impossible for her to ignore injustice. She didn't go out of the way to search it out, but when it appeared on her doorstep she had to do something, like a good housewife who cannot bear dirt and neglect, one might say.

When Mingie had appeared out of nowhere, Mrs. Lee scarcely had to make a decision—much less a determination —to help her and then to help me as well. Once started, she committed herself to an extraordinary degree, many of her friends giving us assistance, too. She was no crusader for tolerance and consideration for Negroes; she was incapable of thinking of herself in such terms. She was taking on a burden but she did not consider it a burden. She was doing what she had to do, and she gave herself to her great task, not with her head—which might well have cautioned her against it—but with all her heart. And her husband was like her, a bit aloof but considerate.

One evening I stayed late to help with preparations for Thanksgiving. Going home by a short cut I sometimes took, I heard a hiss from the thick shrubbery along a fence near a big spreading oak tree. No house was near and no one was about. Next I heard: "Hey! Veanie! Come here. I've got a dollar for you!"

I knew that voice and I knew the head of mop-like brown hair which now was revealed through the shrubbery; the protruding stomach was familiar, too. I ran as fast as I could.

All through the next day, I debated what to do. Mrs. Lee would want me to tell her about it and would not fail to take some action. But it would be a delicate matter for her or Mr. Lee to make trouble for a white man on my behalf. But I was afraid of that man. I thought of all the lonely spots between Mrs. Lee's and my cabin, and how lonely that cabin was with only old Aunt Tiller as my nearest neighbor. So at last I made up my mind and told Miss Rossie.

She recognized the man from my description and she drew

in her breath sharply. "Well, of all the—!" She turned and went out of the kitchen, saying no more to me. When Mr. Lee came home, she told him about it. I heard them talking, and he said to her: "Why, that old guy ought to be run out of town. Rossie, till something's done about him don't let Veanie go home alone after dark."

What they did I don't know, but I was not bothered by that man again.

Christmas was at hand.

In the years before Mingie found Miss Rossie, Christmas had had little meaning for us. When Papa was well and strong and had a job, he always brought little gifts for Mingie and me. But in those years there was always the mama who wasn't our mama; even at Christmas happiness was hard come by. And later when we were alone with Papa and he was paralyzed, Christmas was a day just a little bit more miserable than all the others.

Now I could look forward to it with the happiest anticipation.

The week before Christmas I was helping Miss Rossie and Edie decorate the tree. It stood in the dining room. Exciting boxes, each tied with a dainty bow of ribbon, were lying about everywhere to be piled under the tree.

"Gracious, Miss Rossie!" I exclaimed. "Whoever gets this one is going to be mighty happy!" It was the biggest box of all, with a pyramid of smaller boxes on top of it.

"Never mind that now," Miss Rossie said. "No names are going on until Christmas Eve."

"Go on—tell her, Mother. Tell her whose it is," Edie urged. "Please, I want to know mine, too."

"Miss Rossie," I said, "what day am I going to leave?"

"Let's see—I suppose Friday is best, so you'll be with Mingie on Christmas Eve to help her decorate the baby's tree."

"But, Mother, if she goes, shouldn't she have her present now?" Edie argued.

"On Friday, young lady." Her mother smiled down at her. She knew her little daughter's wiles. "But you're going to wait for Christmas."

I could hardly wait for Friday. I got up early and hurried to Mrs. Lee's. I was grown now—or just about—but the child-like excitement still bubbled up inside me. What would my present be? I hoped it was a suit. I'd more than hoped; I'd hinted to Miss Rossie—and I was a little ashamed of that—that Mingie was getting a new suit for Christmas. Maybe Miss Rossie would give me that beautiful green suit of hers with the wide skirt. . . .

At last the morning was gone, my work done. It was time for me to go. Miss Rossie went to the tree. I watched her hand go down to the big box, the long one underneath all the others. I gasped: "Oh, Miss Rossie—it was mine!"

"I knew it the whole time!" cried Edie triumphantly. "But I didn't tell; did I, Mother?"

"No—but it's a wonder!" Her mother gave her a playful spank.

I asked: "May I open it now?"

"Yes, dear. Since you're going away."

So I slipped the ribbons off the big box, lifted the top, and took out—the green suit! It had been altered to fit me, cleaned, and pressed. Miss Rossie hadn't worn it much. It was just like new. I was so happy I could hardly speak.

"Look some more, Veanie!" said Edie's eager voice. "See? Silk stockings!"

And there they were, too.

I hugged them to my breast. "Oh, Miss Rossie. My first silk stockings!"

144

"You're growing up now, Veanie. There's some in there for Mingie, too."

"And slips and panties and blouses!" cried Edie. "And here"—she thrust another box into my hands—"here's some nuts and candy and fruit cake for Timmy."

"Not for Timmy, darling," Miss Rossie laughed. "Timmy has a new suit."

I hugged the little girl. I wanted to cry.

"Honey, you're going to need an extra suitcase," Miss Rossie said and handed me a big brown one. I saw it was one of Mr. Lee's. "But take good care of it and be sure to bring it back."

The train journey seemed short. I was all gladness, clutching the presents for Mingie and Timmy, anticipating her reaction. I took a cab at my journey's end, and when it stopped in front of Mingie's house, I hopped out and ran ahead of the driver, who came after with my suitcases and packages. Mingie met me at the door with Timmy in her arms. I kissed them and then started back in surprise. "Mingie! I didn't—why, I didn't know you're going to have another baby!"

Mingie managed a smile. "Miss Rossie didn't tell you?"

Again she had told Miss Rossie and not me. Mingie, my sister and twin! I couldn't admit to myself that it was because of my criticism of her and my opposition to her marriage that she hadn't confided in me. My mind stuck on the point that Miss Rossie and Mingie were in a conspiracy against me.

I paid off the cabman. "Sam home?" I asked shortly.

"He's in the house."

Just then Sam came out and I said hello to him as cheerfully as I could, but it was not a good effort.

"Hey, Veanie," he answered glumly and went by and on down the street.

I waited a moment before I asked, "What's wrong with Sam?"

"Nothing, I guess," Mingie said, but avoided my eyes.

I cheered up at the thought of showing off the presents. "Oh, Mingie, wait till you see the lovely things Miss Rossie gave us for Christmas!" And then for a while it was all right with Mingie and with me too, with all the magic of a real Christmas. "Oh, Veanie! Those stockings—real silk!"

"Here's Timmy's suit. Edie picked the material and Miss Rossie made it. She's the sweetest person in the whole world!"

"Couldn't you just love her to death!" Mingie cried. And we buried our hurts by talking about Miss Rossie, remembering.

"Remember, Mingie, when you had something wrong with your leg, how she rubbed it every day?"

"Yes—and when my tonsils were burned out, she stood by me—and had to turn her head away when the doctor hurt me. . . ." We went on and on about our days together with Mrs. Lee. It was a safe subject. At last I said:

"I brought decorations Miss Rossie gave me for Timmy's tree. Let's trim it now; where is it?"

"I—I think Sam is going to get him one today."

I dropped the subject of a Christmas tree. I opened a package of cookies from Mrs. Lee. "Give Timmy one, Mingie."

At once she did, and hungrily the baby tried to chew it.

"Soak it in some milk, Mingie," I said. "Soften it up for him."

"We haven't got any milk right now, Veanie. I think Sam will bring some when he comes back."

No milk! What do you have? I wanted to know, yet could not ask. We were not as once we were with each other. I went down the dark, narrow hallway toward the kitchen. Mingie with Timmy under her arm, followed me and watched me snap a wall button. No light came on. "Is the bulb burned out, Mingie?"

"No—no, the current is off," Mingie said. "I've a lamp; I'll light it."

I knew I was being meddlesome. Miss Rossie had said not to interfere, but Mingie wasn't letting me ask questions. As soon as the lamp was lit, I opened the little icebox in the corner. The odor of damp mold rose from it. In the top where ice should have been, my fingers found a warm, soggy crocus bag. With Mingie silently watching me, I went to the small cabinet and pulled out drawers—empty, one after the other. In the containers on the shelf, I saw a dab of lard, some cornmeal, a cup of flour and a few white potatoes.

Still my sister said nothing, but I knew how she hated to have me inventory her poverty. "Mingie," I asked, "have you had any supper?"

"Yes, Veanie, I had supper."

"The baby?"

"Uh-huh."

"What did you have?"

"I don't remember, honey—it was early this afternoon. We never eat late."

"Aren't you hungry?"

"No—I'm not. Not hungry like you and me used to be, Veanie," my twin reminded me. "And I'm not cookin' crow."

Cookin' crow. That brought me up, hard and quick.

The years rolled back. We were little girls again and there was no Miss Rossie, not yet. We had begun the day hungry, as we always did, but we had been hungry a little too long and we were desperate for ourselves and for Papa. Mingie's plan was to waylay and rob again the same boy whose lunch bucket we had stolen once before.

"But won't he be watchin' for us now?" I was afraid; I was never as bold as Mingie. "An' maybe his mama will be along."

Mingie had thought of that. "Yeah, so we gonna go 'round through the palmetto fiel' this time to fool 'im; an' we hide in the bushes if his mama come."

We posted ourselves and waited. It was a while before we heard a rattling noise coming around the curve of the road. Mingie stuck her head out of the palmettos and hastily drew it back. "Oh, gracious, don' move, Veanie," she warned me in a whisper, " 'cause his mama got 'im on the wagin."

So we were not to snatch his pail today.

The wagon came by, the horse in a slow trot. We sat very still and saw the mother glance toward our house and we were afraid she meant to stop there and make us trouble; but she and the boy—and the lunch pail—went past and soon were out of sight.

Mingie formed another plan. "Come on, Veanie. We go over to the big 'tato field and get us some."

I reminded Mingie of our last visit to that well-fenced field about three quarters of a mile away. A man had been working in it and watching so that we didn't dare creep under the barbed wire anywhere.

"Come on," Mingie merely said again, and I followed her.

When we reached the field, it was still so early that no workers were in sight—though some could be expected; for rows of ripening tomatoes fringed the potato patch and they looked ready for picking. The owner's house was in sight, but it seemed unlikely that we'd been noticed.

We dropped among the weeds, crawled to the fence, and carefully climbed through the wire. We hadn't brought our burlap bag which we usually had when we raided fields, because we'd set out to steal the boy's lunch pail.

"Git tomatoes first," Mingie ordered.

"What'll I put 'em in?"

"Put 'em in ya lap."

148

I picked several of the largest tomatoes and held them in my skirt; Mingie was filling hers with yellow sweet potatoes.

A gun went off.

"Oh, Lordy! Somebody shootin' at us!" Mingie gasped. We flattened on the ground. The gun did not fire again, and we crawled to cover in the thick briars along the drainage ditch; and there we were when a ruddy-faced white man in khaki clothes came from a cornfield beyond the potato patch. He carried a double-barreled shotgun in ready position. We scarcely dared breathe as he came close. Then we saw he wasn't searching for us. His eyes swept higher, he raised his gun, and fired twice far overhead. We heard soft thuds as something fell.

Mingie was holding her hand over my mouth for fear I would cry. The man moved off and Mingie took her hand away.

"He wasn't shootin' at us. He shootin' birds outa the cornfield," she said.

When the man was out of sight, we searched for what he had brought down. "O-o-e-e-e!" we exulted. "Look what we got! Two big crows!"

With the tomatoes and sweet potatoes less honestly come by, they furnished us and Papa a feast. But it was a rank one. The smell and taste of cooked crow was with us for weeks, turning our stomachs.

Cookin' crow—jubilating over the prize of just about the poorest food there is for humans. Mingie, reminding me, had shamed me. She might be poor now, but at least she wasn't cookin' crow.

"I'll buy something, Mingie," I said now. "I'll go to the store and be back in a few minutes."

"Veanie, don't you spend your money. We—"

"It's all right, honey. I've saved up fifteen dollars."

"Fifteen dollars!" Mingie exclaimed. Suddenly her eyes

held tears. We were back together again, the two ragged little girls. Could we have believed, on that morning we so thankfully cooked crow, that we would ever own a fortune of fifteen dollars? We hugged each other.

I went out. On the porch, Sam was scraping his brown loafers on the edge of the rough boards. A quiet steady rain was falling through the big oak trees. "That you, Sam?" I asked somewhat unnecessarily.

"Yeah," Sam answered, his voice as gloomy as the rain that had drenched him.

I don't hate him, I thought. But I couldn't help resenting him for having taken Mingie away from me. I couldn't forgive him for that. I felt sorry for him, and for Mingie, and for myself. This reunion of ours—if we could call it that—had made too plain how far apart Mingie and I had grown. Before Sam appeared, we had shared everything. And now she was having another baby, and had told Miss Rossie, but not me. I stopped feeling sorry for Sam.

Mingie suddenly realized I was going out in the rain without an umbrella and she ran to me with one. I refused it; I told her it didn't matter. That was the mood I was in. I didn't care if I got wet; I wanted to get wet. And I was just about soaked through before I reached the store.

Now I was reminded of the night of the lynching when I coughed into the ground, and when we hid under the house, hugging together on the wet ground, trembling and shivering. We'd gone through everything together, Mingie and me, everything. Until Sam came and Miss Rossie said it was all right for Mingie to marry him.

Was Miss Rossie so wise after all? I was sure I would have been wiser, if Mingie had given me the chance and asked my advice. I would have stopped her from marrying. I would have kept her with me.

At the store I ignored the curious stares of the grocer and the other customers as I went about my business, wet from head to toe, slowly and carefully selecting my purchases. I had fifteen dollars, but how long would that last if it was put to taking care of Mingie and Timmy?

I loaded my arms and I went out again into the rain and sloshed back through the mud to Mingie's.

She met me at the door. "Veanie, darling, you're wringing wet. Why wouldn't you take my umbrella?" She was taking my paper sacks from me, some of them so soaked that they were tearing. "You'll have a cold, Veanie; you'll be sick!" Mingie reproached me. In her mind was what was in mine— our miserable night under the house, my pneumonia, and how Mrs. Lee had taken care of me.

"I made a fire in the stove. There isn't much wood," my sister admitted. "So hurry and dry yourself."

"I'm all right, Mingie. You go on and take care of the baby. I'll cook," I declared. My sacrificial mood was settled on me.

"Timmy's sleeping."

"Well, wake him up. I brought milk; I want to feed him."

"He should sleep now," Mingie insisted.

"Where's Sam?" I asked.

"Oh, he went out again after you left," Mingie replied. She didn't explain, yet I knew. Sam had his pride and he didn't choose to be about when I came back with the dinner he should have provided.

A little sense returned to me. I took off my wet clothes and changed into dry ones, leaving Mingie to start the dinner. When we were working together, side by side as we used to, it was a little better. Yet still it was so different! I could feel Mingie on the defensive against me. But when Timmy woke up she let me feed him.

Sam came in.

"You're just in time, Sam," I said brightly. "We've got pork chops for supper—pork chops and sweet potatoes, your favorite. There's a chicken for Christmas dinner."

Sam only stared at me.

"Come on and eat, Sam," Mingie begged him.

"I don't want nothin'," Sam said, and went into the bedroom. Mingie followed him. A little later she came back, alone. "He just wants to sleep," she said sadly. We sat down to our supper and neither of us felt comfortable with the other. We ate, but it might just as well have been crow we were eating.

Sam went out again and returned with a little tree for Timmy. The three of us trimmed it and worked up a little Christmas spirit. On Christmas Day, Sam sat at the table with us and ate dinner, but good feeling and happiness did not sit down at that table. For me, the thought kept intruding that this was at least partly my fault; I was letting Miss Rossie down. I hadn't learned the lesson she had never had to speak: you have to love when you give, else your gift becomes an affront.

I pushed the guilty feeling away. I refused to look at it.

Later, on that Christmas day, I tried to persuade my sister to leave her husband and come back to me.

"No, Veanie. I can't."

"You can, Mingie. I've enough to pay your fare back."

"What about Timmy—and this baby that's coming?"

I said confidently: "I'll take care of all of you."

"But what would Miss Rossie say?"

I weakened before that. "You can tell her how things are, or I'll tell her for you. She'll understand, Mingie."

"She'll understand, all right, but maybe different from the way you do. She told me things might get hard, even awful hard. But I mustn't run away, like we ran away from school.

I mustn't run away from these things, whatever happened."

"Did she really say 'whatever happened'?"

"Well, maybe it was 'almost whatever happened.' But I know she meant more than—than this here."

I knew it too. I knew that Miss Rossie meant what she had said, and meant it only for the best for Mingie. But Miss Rossie wasn't Mingie's sister and twin; she couldn't know how it was. But I hoped that in time Miss Rossie would understand.

14

ON SUNDAY I took the late train home, arriving long after dark to spend a dreary, lonely night. Early in the morning I was at Mrs. Lee's.

She was getting up and she called: "Is that you, Veanie?"

"Yes, ma'am, Miss Rossie."

"Will you start the coffee, honey—and put on some grits? I'll be there in a minute."

"All right, ma'am," I replied, as much like the old way as I could make it. But I was feeling different than ever I had felt toward her.

Mr. Lee came out of the bedroom first. "Well, and how's our runaway cook making out?" he said in his cheery way.

"Fine, Mr. Lee. How are you, sir?"

"Oh, the old man's going to live, I think. Did you have a good Christmas, Veanie?"

"Yes, sir."

Mrs. Lee, coming from the bedroom, remarked, "You don't

sound very enthusiastic." But I glossed over things in my replies to her questions, and to Edie's when she joined in. Miss Rossie knew I was evading, and I guess Mr. Lee did too. When he left for his office, Miss Rossie went with him to the door, as she always did, and they talked in low, hurried tones. Then Miss Rossie sent Edie to play with a little friend on the porch and came back to the kitchen.

"What did you find so wrong, Veanie?"

"Oh, Miss Rossie, just about everything!" burst from me. Miss Rossie heard me out to the last sob of my lament. That's what it was—a bemoaning for Mingie that things had to be so hard for her.

"Does she have to stay with Sam, Miss Rossie?" I appealed. "Mingie'd leave Sam, I know, if you'd just tell her it's all right. Oh, Miss Rossie, I know she would!"

She looked straight at me and said quietly: "Veanie, you want me to tell a wife and a mother it's right to leave her husband just because things are difficult?"

I had to avoid her eyes. And what she had said seemed to me unfair. I hadn't asked her that; I'd only asked her to say it was right for Mingie to leave Sam.

"Veanie," said Miss Rossie, "you just haven't given up yet. You want so much to have Mingie back that you let yourself exaggerate everything you saw. You must remember that Mingie is pregnant again, and that alone might cause her to get thinner for a while. Timmy's a year old, and growing, so he'd be thinner too, and—"

"But, Miss Rossie, they didn't have anything even for Christmas, not a thing! And wouldn't have if I hadn't come." And after going all over it again, I ended with: "Oh, Miss Rossie, I know that Mingie's only waiting for you to tell her it's right to leave Sam."

"Veanie, you're old enough to understand the meaning of

marriage. It's the relationship upon which so many others depend. Destroy it, or take it lightly, and suddenly there's nothing left. I know that many people—privileged people— do take it lightly. But others must not be guided by them, especially not Mingie and Sam."

I knew what she meant and she knew I would grasp it without her having to put it more plainly and painfully. A charge against the colored folk was irresponsibility in the marriage relationship. For the sake of others as well as for them, she would—if she could—stop Mingie and Sam from adding substance to it.

I knew that, but it didn't help to know it. Mingie wasn't just anybody. Mingie was Mingie, my sister and twin, a part of myself.

In February, Mingie's second boy, Ted, was born.

I had stopped harassing Mrs. Lee about Mingie, but between my visit to my sister and Ted's birth, I'd worried myself sick trying to plan some way of getting Mingie and her babies home without offending Mrs. Lee. I am amazed when I think back over my persistence. I'd lost weight and Mrs. Lee mentioned it.

"Yes, ma'am, I have. I weigh ninety-eight. I was up to a hundred and three once."

"Five pounds. That's too much for a growing girl to lose. You'd better drink more milk."

"I'm drinking a lot of milk and eating plenty. It's not that, Miss Rossie," I replied, and would have taken this opportunity to launch into what "it" was, but she forestalled me by moving away.

I knew she'd sent presents to Mingie for the new baby and I was sure she'd given other help. But she was leaving it to Mingie and Sam to solve their own problems. Too ready an acceptance of a position of dependence was another charge against my people; Mrs. Lee would not encourage it, hard as it was for her not to, in the case of Mingie.

A few weeks later, when I said I wanted to go up and visit my sister again, Mrs. Lee neither assented nor offered objection. I arranged to be gone for three days but I was back at the end of two.

"Veanie!" Mrs. Lee exclaimed, as I entered the door. "I didn't expect you today. Didn't you go to see Mingie?"

"Yes, ma'am, but I'm back."

"How is the new baby?"

"He's all right, Miss Rossie, and Timmy's all right."

"And Mingie?"

"She's about the same."

"The same as when you were there before?"

"Yes, Miss Rossie."

"How was Sam this time?"

"All right—the same."

"Why didn't you stay longer?"

"It wasn't any good my staying there, Miss Rossie."

She didn't ask for details. I would have told her how desolate that house was up there in Lakeland, how little there was to eat, how thin and sad Mingie was, how Timmy's bones were sticking out. . . . But Miss Rossie knew what I was after, and she gave me no opportunity to reopen the subject of Mingie's leaving Sam.

For the next few months I saved every penny I could. I think Miss Rossie knew it and guessed the purpose I had in mind, but she didn't say anything to me. I made other preparations, in the old cabin, and at last I was ready.

The day came when I didn't go to Mrs. Lee's, and I hadn't given her any sort of notice that I might not be coming. That was mean and it bothered me, but I hadn't been able to think of a better way to do it; I couldn't have lied to Miss Rossie's face.

What Mrs. Lee did, I learned later from Aunt Tiller, whose rheumatism kept her home from work that day.

Mrs. Lee drove up in her car and gave the usual familiar signal. She repeated it several times and then slipped from under the steering wheel and came up on the porch where she called my name. She tried the door, found it locked, and was trying to decide what to do when Aunt Tiller called: "Mis' Lee, ma'am, Veanie, she ain' there; she gone."

Mrs. Lee went swiftly across the sand to Aunt Tiller's. To her questions, Aunt Tiller could only repeat: "Veanie ain' there; she done gone."

"Gone where, Aunt Tiller?"

"I don' know, ma'am. The las' I see Veanie, she had two suitcases. She toted 'em lightlike, so it couldna been too much in 'em. I sho' thought you knowed."

"I didn't," Mrs. Lee replied. "She said nothing to me about going away. Didn't she say anything to you?"

"No, ma'am. Not nary a word. Since she so secret 'bout it, I reckin she gone to get married like the other one. They was mighty close, you know. An' twins don' live too good 'thout one another, so they say."

"Veanie wouldn't have gone off to get married without telling me, Aunt Tiller," Mrs. Lee said.

Aunt Tiller wasn't so sure. "They's pecul'y childun. Always was, ma'am," she said, and seeing how hurt Mrs. Lee seemed, she added: "You sho is been good to 'em, ma'am. Ain't nobody like you. Neither of 'em ought ever vex you like this."

Aunt Tiller scolded me the next morning when, having returned, I went to talk to her before going to Mrs. Lee. I was more than two hours late when I arrived, and Mrs. Lee heard me and called: "Veanie?"

"Yes, ma'am, Miss Rossie."

"Come here, Veanie, and tell me where you've been."

I slowly approached her bedroom door. I wasn't afraid of her. Ashamed was nearer to it. I was ashamed and defiant, too, for I was sure I was right in what I'd done, if wrong in the way I'd done it.

Mrs. Lee was beside her bed, sorting and folding up linen, and she didn't stop. She merely glanced over her shoulder at me as I halted at the door and she said, "Well?" in a very matter-of-fact manner.

I stepped into the room where she could see me, but she gave all her attention to the linen.

"Miss Rossie—ma'am—Mingie and the babies are here."

"They are?" She was still folding.

"Yes, ma'am."

"When did they come?"

"This morning."

Mrs. Lee made no comment. She simply stood there, bending a little as she folded bed sheets. My defiance melted and left me only shame and guilt. I fell to my knees on the floor. "Oh, Miss Rossie! Miss Rossie!"

"What is it, Veanie?"

"Miss Rossie, you told me not to interfere with Mingie and Sam, and I did."

"I knew it—after I'd talked with Aunt Tiller."

"Oh, Miss Rossie; she told me—how you come lookin' for me. She told me—reminded me how you've always looked after me—Mingie and me."

Without looking at me, Mrs. Lee said evenly: "Get up off the floor, Veanie. That's not necessary."

"But Miss Rossie, I want you to forgive me."

"Get up, Veanie."

I did so. "I didn't really make Mingie leave Sam, Miss Rossie," I said. "She was all ready to."

"She told you that?"

"No—no, ma'am—not exactly," I had to admit, "but she acted it."

"Has she come to stay?"

"Yes, ma'am. I brought all of her stuff."

"What did Sam say about it?"

"He wasn't there. He had gone to work."

"He's still working on the train?"

"Yes, Miss Rossie."

"And you didn't wait for him to come back from work?"

"No, ma'am," I admitted and felt guiltier. But I wouldn't, not even if I could, undo what I'd done. Mrs. Lee felt it.

She asked: "Why didn't Mingie bring the baby to see me?"

"She was sort of ashamed—worried—because she didn't know how you'd feel, Miss Rossie."

"Well, you tell her to bring him tomorrow. I won't have time to go out today."

"Yes, ma'am. Oh, she'll be so glad, Miss Rossie! I can tell Mingie it's all right?"

"Of course I'll be glad to see Mingie and her babies. There's only this I have to say since they're here: having done what you have, Veanie, don't you feel that Mingie herself should decide whether she wants to stay or return to her husband?"

"Yes, ma'am."

"You mean it, Veanie?"

"Yes, ma'am."

"And you'll remember it?"

I promised that, too. And of course I did remember it; how could I forget? But I went back on the promise when Sam appeared.

That was the next day. I met him at the door of the cabin. He told me he'd come for Mingie. I stared at him for a few seconds before I called: "Mingie, here's Sam."

Mingie came to the center of the floor and stood looking at him through the door. I turned sidewise between them and leaned against the panel. I just couldn't leave them alone, as I'd promised Mrs. Lee to do.

Mingie kept quiet and Sam said not a word; they just stood there, looking at each other, with me between them. Finally I said: "Mingie, honey, he came for you. Do you want to go back with him?"

Mingie moved her head in a way that might be taken to mean no; but she didn't make it too sure and she still didn't speak.

My eyes flashed to Sam's.

"Come on out here, Mingie," he gruffly commanded. He stuffed his hands into his pockets and strode to the other end of the porch.

I pressed back to let Mingie by, but otherwise I didn't move. I didn't leave them to themselves. I watched them every second as they sat side by side on the steps, talking. Sam kept his voice low and Mingie scarcely whispered, so I couldn't make out what either of them said, but I watched them every minute and I could see Mingie weakening. Except for staying right there, I didn't interfere.

Sam got up and without a word to me, without a glance, he trudged off through the rain-soaked sand of the yard. Mingie jumped up, ran past me into the house, and threw herself sobbing on the bed.

"What did he say, Mingie?"

"He—he told me to be ready when he comes back for me—it's his last day on his run to this end. Then he's going north."

North! That meant, if Mingie went with him, she and the

babies would be even further from me than ever. I'd *never* see them.

"Mingie, do you *want* to go?" I demanded, and kept arguing as if the decision of whether or not she should stay with her husband was merely a matter of *want* and not of right and duty, love and responsibility. I knew it wasn't and I knew I was going against Mrs. Lee and got so ashamed that I stopped suddenly. Mingie sat up and asked: "What was you going to say, Veanie?"

"That's all, Mingie," I replied, and saw that what I had already said had been enough. "You're not going a way, way off with Sam, are you, Mingie?"

"I guess—not."

"Then you tell Miss Rossie yourself, Mingie. Remember she said for you to bring Ted to show her today."

"I'll go with you when you're ready."

"Mingie!" I made a decision. "I'm not going to Miss Rossie's today."

"Why not, Veanie? We can take both Teddy and Timmy; doesn't Miss Rossie want us to?"

"Miss Rossie said for you only to bring Teddy," I replied and that was the truth—except for the "only" I put in. I knew Mrs. Lee had meant both children. But she hadn't said so, and I built on that to persuade Mingie it wasn't really convenient for Mrs. Lee to have the visit today. The truth was that I didn't want Mingie to see Mrs. Lee at all, until after Sam had come back and been sent away. So I managed that, and I managed more.

"I tell you what, Mingie," I said. "You and the babies go over to Aunt Tiller's and stay until I come home, and don't go out on the porch or into the yard if you see Sam coming before he said he would. And don't let Aunt Tiller know why you came."

I wasn't sure I could trust Mingie to do that but I had to take the chance. Besides, I was pretty sure I'd be back before Sam came. So I hurried off to Mrs. Lee's. She asked me at once why Mingie hadn't come with the babies.

"She—she's going to bring them tomorrow, Miss Rossie," I said, trying to hide my uneasiness.

"Did Sam come?"

"Ye-yes, ma'am, but he didn't stay long."

"Is he coming back?"

I could not tell her the direct lie, but I replied: "I don't quite know." And I managed not to give her satisfactory answers to other questions.

I was unhappy about it and so was Mrs. Lee, but she stopped questioning me. I hurried through my work. When I asked to go, she offered to drive me home, as she often did. I thanked her but told her I'd walk.

"What are you up to, Veanie?" she asked. "You've never refused a ride."

I tried to laugh.

"Whatever you're doing, Veanie, let it be approved by a good conscience."

"Yes-yes, ma'am, Miss Rossie."

I found Mingie and the babies at home. Mingie had taken the babies to Aunt Tiller's and kept them there until Aunt Tiller went off to her work. Aunt Tiller had had her suspicions. "Looka here, honey—you ain' hidin' f'om yo' husban', is you?" she inquired, and gave her advice. "You mayse well stay with that one 'cause yo' ain' gon' fin' nary one no better. They's all jesta like. These li'l boys here need 'im, chile."

Sam hadn't come yet and I went on with my plan, getting Mingie and the babies to go back to Aunt Tiller's empty house where we shut ourselves in and waited.

It was a long wait during hours of heavy rain. At last there was the usual blast of the whistle for the blind crossing and a black engine nosed into sight and slowed for the brush-hidden corner. Sam was standing in the wide-open door of the baggage car. Both Mingie and I saw him.

As the train screeched to a crawling pace, he swung out by one foot and one hand, leaped to the ground, and ran along beside the cars. He waved to a workmate, stopped, looked toward our house, and swiftly approached it, his face bowed and shaded by his black-bibbed cap that dripped with rain.

As I watched, my heart was thumping and I could imagine Mingie's was. But I kept her there beside me.

Sam went to the steps and up them to the porch where he scuffed his feet; he was eying the closed door. He rapped on it, rapped again, and called. He tried it and found it locked. After a while, he wheeled about and went back down the steps and across the yard to the train. I remember how the wet sand fell from his heels behind him as he walked away. I wonder what it is that Mingie remembers, today.

I had my arms about her, she was crying so. But—she'd let Sam go.

Later I said, "Now we've got to tell Miss Rossie everything. I'll do it, Mingie," I offered, "and I'll tell her all I did, too."

"I'll tell Miss Rossie you really aren't the reason," Mingie answered. "I'll tell her so she'll see— No." She weakened. "I just won't say anything unless she asks me. Then I'll tell her the truth."

"Yes, Mingie. That would be better," I agreed.

Mingie was miserable for a long time, and so was I. At night, hearing her sometimes turning restlessly in bed, I would pray to God that I had done right. I was afraid that to the end of my days I would be haunted by the picture of Sam plodding desolately through the sand back to the train while

I was holding Mingie. Did I do right? If I did, was it for the right reasons, or were my reasons wrong and selfish?

Much later I thought to ask Mingie why she and Sam had been so poor when he'd had a good job.

"Well, sometimes there was a layoff," she said. "But even when he was working, it was the same, or just about."

I thought for a while. Then I asked: "Mingie, did he maybe have other women?"

"Oh, no!" She was shocked.

"And he didn't drink—I know that."

"No."

It was puzzling. Maybe Sam had got into debt furnishing that nice house up in Lakeland? Maybe he'd had other troubles. . . .

"Mingie, didn't you ask him why there wasn't any money?"

"But, Veanie, I just couldn't. He was a grown man."

I felt a little better after that. Sam had not been the right kind of husband, and Mingie had been too young to be a wife.

15

NOTHING THAT either of us said could make Mrs. Lee feel that Mingie had been right in ending her marriage; and she did not accept it as the fact it proved to be. For a long time she kept hoping that Mingie and Sam would reunite.

We had hurt her, both Mingie and I, disappointed her. But she didn't go on and on about it. There was no anger or bitterness in her. She didn't make us feel we had sinned against her. She didn't make us feel guilty or uncomfortable with her. She went on, as always.

She helped me to make no fewer than five new dresses for the opening of school on the Tuesday after Labor Day.

I was putting one on and Mingie was watching me enviously. "Veanie, I sure wish I could go back to school again," she said, her eyes a little sad. "But not even Miss Rossie thinks I should right now. Later, perhaps, she says."

" 'Perhaps' with Miss Rossie means you will," I said with more confidence than I felt.

166

"Oh, I know that!"

So Mingie was at home with her babies. I was back in school and going to Mrs. Lee's after school.

Soon after the start of the term I was in the kitchen getting supper when Edie came in on tiptoe. Her blue eyes were impish. "Veanie, I've got a great big secret that you don't know," she whispered, holding a finger to her lips and looking back through the door. "Mother is lying down. Do you know why?"

I started across the dining room, seized with a sudden fear. "Is she sick, Edie?"

Edie caught my apron. "No. You mustn't bother her, Veanie. She's not sick, not really and truly."

"Then what's the matter?"

"No, I can't tell right now. That's the secret. Mother told me last night—Daddy, too."

"Edie," I threatened, "if you don't tell me I won't fix your favorite for supper."

"French fries, Veanie?"

I nodded. "No secret, no French fries."

"All right. But you've got to promise not to breathe a word."

"I promise," I said solemnly.

"Veanie, we–are–going–to–have–a baby brother!" She tapped each word on my arm with her fingers. "Surprised?" Then she laughed happily because my face showed her what a wonderful surprise it was, and what a glorious secret.

When I could talk, I got out one word: "When?"

"Let's see—in about five years—months, I mean."

"How do you know it will be a brother? It might be another sweet little girl just like you." I snuggled her to me.

"No, it isn't. Daddy says it's a boy. And he said I was a girl, before I came—see?"

When Miss Rossie came to the dining room for supper, I

watched her carefully and anxiously asked: "How do you feel now, Miss Rossie?"

"I feel all right, honey. Just a little dizzy, but it's all gone now." She caught the back of a chair and was about to pull it out when I stepped quickly forward and did it for her.

"Well, thank you, Veanie," she said. Her brows arched and a bright smile lightened her face as she glanced at me. "My, honey, why all the gentle service so suddenly? I'm not ill."

"Yes, ma'am—but you're—" I stopped, but she guessed what had happened and exclaimed: "Oh, has she told you, too?"

"You mean about the new—new baby?"

"Yes. Our Edie is just like a darn little mockingbird—keeps nothing. I heard her on the phone telling Grandma early this morning. Yes, Veanie, five months and there'll be another bawler in this house."

"Oh, Miss Rossie. I hope it's another little Edie."

"We're hoping for a boy this time, though; and I'm planning all blue and white for it. If it turns up a 'she,' she'll certainly wear 'he' things—for a long time, anyway."

The next day I started sewing for the expected baby. I made a white nightie so it would be right for a boy or girl. I made other things too, and so did Mingie. I looked after Miss Rossie as if she were herself a baby, and sometimes she became impatient with me and laughed me away. In the Lee house as the months passed the quiet happiness rose to a tiptoe sort of excitement, and poor Mr. Lee would be glowing one minute and the next minute he'd be just about gnawing his nails from worry.

"Veanie." He'd erupt into the kitchen and suddenly stop. "How's she been today?"

"Fine, Mr. Lee."

"Veanie, are you *sure*?"

"Yes, sir. Just fine."

He'd go out and I'd hear him talking to her. Then he'd be back again. "Veanie, was Edie quiet today?"

"Good as gold, Mr. Lee."

"Veanie—"

It was a boy that was born four and a half months after Edie told me the great secret. Robert Milton Lee was his name on the register; but Sonny Boy he became from the day his mother brought him home from the hospital. That was Mingie's doing. "I've always loved to hear Mr. Lee play that piece, Miss Rossie," Mingie said. "And somehow Sonny Boy seems just right for him."

And so he became Sonny Boy, a little person much closer to us than a formal Robert could become.

Quickly he began to influence all our lives—very particularly Mingie's children. They adored him, and he them. He played with them when Mingie brought them to Mrs. Lee's, and when Miss Rossie drove me home and had Sonny Boy with her she would stay a while to let him play in the palmettos with Teddy and Timmy. Sonny Boy knew our neighborhood and neighbors just about as well as he knew his own.

I often think of a birthday—Sonny Boy's fourth. A party was being arranged for him at home, but he didn't like that. "Mutter," he said, "I don't want my party now. I want to go to Mingie's."

"You can go tomorrow," said his mother. "You have a lot of friends coming to see you today."

"No. Ted and Timmy want me to come now. I know it."

"Now, honey, that's not being a good boy. What would the children say if they came and brought you presents and you weren't here. Would that be nice?"

"N-no." The little boy thought quickly. "You can take and put them in my wagon!" He ran out to the porch and hustled in his big red wagon. "See, Mutter? It will take a lot of presents."

"But mother can't do that, honey. Now, if you don't want a party, all of the ice cream and cookies and candy and little hats can go right back to the store."

That was too hard. Sonny Boy could not bear the thought of giving up all those wonderful things. He raised his blond head, looking up at his mother, and asked: "Mutter, can Timmy and Ted come to my party?"

I often wonder what, exactly, were the thoughts that ran through Miss Rossie's mind as she looked down at her beautiful little son. How could she explain to him that little colored boys he played with couldn't come to the same party with little white boys he played with? A four-year-old would never understand that, and certainly not Sonny Boy.

She bent down to him. "Darling, listen. Timmy and Ted can't come today. But you can save them some of all the good things and take it over to them tomorrow."

"Why? Why can't they come? I want them."

Miss Rossie rose and thought for a while. "All right," she said. "They can come. But they'll be in the kitchen helping Mingie and Veanie."

"Why?"

She sighed. "That's the way it has to be," she said in a tone that permitted no further why's.

After midmorning I hurried home to tell Mingie not to leave Timmy and Ted with Aunt Tiller, as we'd arranged, but to bring them with her when she came to help me with the party; and I told her how it had happened that they were asked to come.

"Mingie, do you think it will be all right for them to be there with all those white children?" I was beginning to feel worried about it.

Mingie was more hopeful. "I think so, Veanie—if we keep them with us. I'll talk to them." And she did so, when we had them in the big tub, scrubbing them clean. "Now, Timmy, Ted—you must be real sweet and real careful up there to-day. If the children say anything to you, talk nice to them; and if they call you names, don't either of you say anything back to them. You see, they don't know you like Sonny Boy does and they'll be different. So you both stay right with me in the kitchen until they all leave. If Sonny wants you to play with him, tell him you've got to help mother and Veanie."

Neither of Mingie's sons asked why; they understood. Timmy inquired only: "Will we get some of the cake and ice cream, Mother?"

"Why, sure, honey. You know Miss Rossie is going to give you a real big helping."

We got them into their short blue Sunday suits which Mrs. Lee had given them and we polished their white shoes. As we arrived ahead of time, Sonny and Timmy and Ted had a few minutes to play together. The small guests began to appear, accompanied by their mothers; and there were a few older children, invited by Edie. Mingie and I took Timmy and Ted into the kitchen, but Sonny followed us. "Now, Sonny," I said, "you go and meet the children. Timmy and Ted will stay here."

He took Mingie's boys by the hand and tried to pull them toward the parlor. "No, Veanie; they're going, too. I want them."

"They can't go in there, Sonny. The other children don't know them."

"Billie knows them. He wants them to come."

"Billie, Mrs. Porter's son, came trotting from the dining room with a big package in his arms. "Here, Sonny! Here's your birthday present!" He laid the box on Sonny Boy's out-stretched arms.

"I'm going to see it right now!" Sonny Boy decided. He set it on the floor and started tearing away the paper.

Billie took the opportunity to exhibit to Timmy and Ted the new gadgets and trinkets he carried in the pockets of his first long-pants suit. He handed Timmy a small spinning top. "Here, you can have this. I've got a new one," he said, and added, "Ted, you'll have to play with it some, too. I haven't got another one for you."

Sonny had his big box open and discovered a gun-metal-black locomotive and four passenger coaches. "Look, Timmy! Look, Ted! A train! He gave me a train!" He gathered up the engine and cars and started for the back door. "Come on, Billie! Timmy! Let's go out and build a track!"

Mingie tried to stop them and so did I. But all four were against us and we didn't want to start a disturbance, so they got out and made straight for the sand box.

Meanwhile, Miss Rossie, having greeted the guests, was looking about for Sonny. She found me alone in the kitchen. "Where's Sonny Boy, Veanie? Where's Mingie and her children?"

I explained and she went out to the sand box where the four little boys, black and white, were flat on their stomachs, side by side, fashioning for themselves a railroad track and tunnel.

Mrs. Lee looked at Mingie but didn't say a word of reproach. She just shook her head and smiled.

"Look, Mutter!" Sonny exclaimed jubilantly. "My train is going through this tunnel to the big city. Timmy and Billie are building the city."

"Yes, darling," Mrs. Lee said gently, "but you've got to

come inside for a little while. And look at your nice clean suits—all of you!"

But it was too late. The children in the house had discovered where Sonny was and they streamed out to see what was going on. I went out the back door, too. Mingie well understood what she ought to do. "Timmy! Ted!" she beckoned them. "Come here."

"No, Mingie!" Sonny promptly objected. "Timmy's got to build my city."

Then one little girl, about six years old, wheeled about from the circle around the sand box. "Mother!" she shrilled. "There's two little nigger boys out here, playing with Sonny!"

Her mother and the others came to see it.

Greatly as I loved Mrs. Lee for other things she had done for us, never did I love and admire her more than at that moment. There she stood, before her friends, in the false position of having seemed to have arranged that colored children would play with her own, and perhaps with theirs, at a party to which she had invited them. Of course she hadn't planned this; she'd planned to prevent it. But she would not—and she did not—spare herself by going into explanations. She chose to spare Mingie and me—and Mingie's children.

"Now, if you all will go back inside," she quietly said to her guests, "I'll get Sonny dusted off and bring him in to you."

As the white children and their mothers returned to the house, I looked up worriedly at Mrs. Lee. "'Miss Rossie, do you want Mingie to take hers home?" I asked.

"No. They'll be all right. Don't worry about what's happened, Veanie. Come on in and start putting the candy in the cups. Mingie can sort of keep the boys with her on the porch."

Mingie did it; but she couldn't keep Sonny Boy from running to the porch, persistently trying to get Timmy and Ted to join the other children.

At serving time, he appeared with his dish of ice cream and placed it on the porch table where Ted and Timmy were eating. One by one, three other boys followed him. All went well for a while. I was in the dining room, helping serve the other children, when I heard a scream. A five-year-old boy ran from the kitchen, holding his nose and yelling: "Mommy! Sonny hit me!"

His mother cuddled him. "Well, now, it's not that bad. I'm sure. Perhaps he didn't mean to hurt you, darling. Let's be a big boy and don't cry."

"Oh, I'm terribly sorry!" Mrs. Lee apologized to the mother and hurried out to the porch to learn what had happened.

Sonny Boy sat quietly munching a crisp cookie. Without looking up at his mother, he explained: "Well, he said Timmy and Ted were 'niggers' and I socked him."

A few days later, it happened the other way around.

We had Sonny at our house playing with Ted and Timmy. Some of our neighbors' children joined them in one of their wild games, which was cops and robbers one minute and cowboys and Indians the next. Little boys were dying, dodging, shooting, and hopping over palmetto roots in wild abandon when somebody—not Sonny or Ted or Timmy—broke the unwritten rules by coming again to life and action while he was still supposed to be dead. An argument started in which a bigger boy tried to bully Sonny. Timmy, who was as big as, but no bigger than, the bully, promptly pushed him over a stump, and he ran bawling home to his mother, who came to us in no little anger. Mingie scolded her son. "He was fixing to beat up Sonny," Timmy said, "and I got him first."

16

ONE MORNING a horn sounded in front of our cabin. I was getting up and Mingie was waking up. Since there had been only one long toot, we wondered who it could be. It sounded like the horn on Miss Rossie's car, but she always gave two short toots as a signal.

We heard footsteps on the porch and a quick rap on the door. Dressed only in my slip, I stooped and peered through the crack under the door. I saw white, crepe-soled shoes. "Mr. Lee, is that you?"

"Yes, Veanie."

"I'll be ready in a moment, Mr. Lee!" I cried and as I put on a dress, I called to Mingie: "Mr. Lee is here. Something must be the matter, Mingie. I'm going."

I opened the door and when I saw Mr. Lee, I knew something was very much the matter.

"Veanie, Mrs. Lee is very sick," he told me. "She wants one of you to stay with the children until she gets home from the hospital."

"Hospital?" I gasped. "Oh, Mr. Lee. No!"

"Are you ready to come, Veanie?"

"Oh, yes sir!" I replied, but for a minute I was in a panic. "Mingie, Miss Rossie is sick—going to the hospital!" I relayed to my sister. "Hurry—help me get my clothes. I'm going to stay with the children."

Mingie kept better control of herself, but her voice shook as she asked: "Mr. Lee, is she very ill?"

"Well, Mingie, we don't know how serious it is just yet. The doctor thinks it may be appendicitis and an operation may be necessary. He's waiting with her to take her to the hospital as soon as I get back."

We wasted no time. Mingie and I said not another word. We only looked at each other, each with the same terrible thought in that look: suppose Miss Rossie died!

I jumped into the car and Mr. Lee had little to say to me. He gave all his attention to driving so as to save every possible second on the way home.

Miss Rossie was in her bedroom. He went in to speak to her before he signaled to me.

She was lying on her bed and she turned her flushed face to me. She seemed burning with fever but the usual bright smile was on her lips. It almost broke me; I dropped to my knees beside the bed. "Oh, Miss Rossie; I'm so, so sorry! How do you feel now, Miss Rossie?" I appealed to her, as if somehow I wanted her blessing, as if it was I who needed her help.

"I feel a lot better than a while ago, honey. The pains have stopped now."

"I'm so glad, Miss Rossie!" But I knew I never could tell from her, whether or not she suffered.

Her hand closed on mine. "Take good care of the children, Veanie—and don't let Sonny Boy rule you. Mr. Lee will call from the office during the day to see how you're getting along. And will you count up Mr. Lee's shirts and the children's clothes—"

"Yes, ma'am, Miss Rossie. I know what's to be done," I assured her. "And I'll watch the children every minute."

"I know you will. But you mustn't let Sonny rule you," she repeated. "You love him, I know; but it's not loving him the right way to let him get away with it."

"No, ma'am; yes, ma'am, I mean."

"If you need anything for the kitchen and the children, just run over to the store and charge it."

"Yes, ma'am."

Mr. Lee, who had left me alone with her, returned to the room. "Well, sweetheart," he said as she looked at him, "shall we go to the hospital now?"

It wasn't like the other time she went to the hospital; then she wasn't sick and I wasn't afraid. Now I was. An operation! No one denied there was danger in any operation. There could be complications. . . . Danger meant, of course, danger of death; it meant Miss Rossie might die.

How she'd made over the world for Mingie and me! And how the happiness she'd brought us depended upon her remaining in it! She made over the world for everyone about her. Who could bear to think of that house—of Mr. Lee and the children—without her?

It was a bad time, a time of fears that must not show or be spoken for the sake of the children and Mr. Lee. In due course, I was told that Mrs. Lee had "come through" the operation; her condition was "good"; she was "resting comfortably." But somehow I was not reassured; nor was Mingie. Later I was to learn—or rather to realize from such cautions as "It will be quite a while before Mrs. Lee is herself again"—that her operation had not been just an ordinary one.

She herself was not told; but I'm sure she realized it, too. However, only in physical energy was she ever less than "herself"; her quick, loving smile and her thoughtfulness never forsook her.

"I'm very proud of you, Veanie. You took such good care of the children and of everything here while I was gone," she said to me when, at last, she was back in her own bed. I reached over to smooth the sheet and she put her hand on mine. She was laughing. "And now you make it so easy for me I might not want to get out of this bed, I warn you."

"You just stay in it, Miss Rossie. I'll always be right here," I replied, feeling so choked that I scarcely could say it.

Mingie's feelings matched mine. She didn't bring her boys to the house for fear they'd disturb Miss Rossie, but as often as she could get Aunt Tiller to look after Ted and Timmy, Mingie came over.

"Ah—you two are just spoiling me," Mrs. Lee would say. "You're stricter than the doctor. My stitches are all out and I feel fine."

She was gaining strength; she was up and about, but I stayed on to make sure she didn't attempt too much.

Long after the doctor had declared her fully recovered, Mingie and I would be shaken by a sudden fear, and then it would be hard to sleep. So much had Miss Rossie come to mean to us that she was a part of us, as dear and meaningful as Mingie and I were to each other.

Some day Mingie or I, or both of us together, would leave Miss Rossie. Already we knew that. Even Mingie's premature attempt to make a life of her own had been a reaching out to a world wider than Miss Rossie's house and garden. Sooner or later we'd both leave her, but the thought that she might leave us—die—was a shattering one.

As little girls we had been forced to live our own life. It

had taught us a lesson, hard though it had been. We could never be entirely dependent, and Miss Rossie had never wanted us to be. She had not been acting fairy godmother to two little waifs. She had been helping two girls to grow up.

Some day we would leave her and try to give to others what she had given us. But not yet. And please God, don't take her from us; don't take her from a world that needs her so!

"Veanie, I love you." His arms around me, and the sweetness of it, the marvel. Now at last I knew what Mingie must have felt for Sam. A decision was before me, the most important of my life.

I had met Clyde at a school dance and had liked him at once, and he had liked me. He was handsome and well mannered, attractive to the girls and respected by the men; and he was attentive to me—and something more. We had known each other now for several months, and I was as certain as a girl can be that very soon now I must say yes—or no. Clyde had a good job which sometimes took him as far away as Collier City, and he was going to move there. If I married him, I would live in Collier City. I wouldn't like that, but it was nothing to stand in the way of marrying, under ordinary circumstances. But the circumstances just then weren't ordinary.

I'd brought Clyde to meet Miss Rossie and she had liked him. She said he had impressed her as not only a pleasant young man but a dependable one. I told her he was; and he was good and loving—and lovable.

"Then, Veanie, you love him?" she asked.

"Miss Rossie, I don't know!" I evaded.

She studied me. "You're thinking of Mingie's marriage," she said. "And of looking after Mingie and the children until they're old enough so Mingie can go to work. And you're thinking of me, too; you don't want to leave me while I'm still not entirely strong and well. Is that right, Veanie?"

She knew—but not everything, perhaps. How could she know the pain that even the thought of leaving her caused me? How could she know all my mixed-up feelings about Mingie? And then there was school—could she know how much that meant to me? I was in my senior year and would soon be a high school graduate with all that would mean: a lifelong advantage in applying for a job. And I dreamed of college, too. How I was ever to accomplish college, I did not know. But I would have to dismiss it even from my dreams if I married and went away from Miss Rossie. Miss Rossie had a way of making dreams come true.

She said: "Veanie, it's your own life and your own happiness you must think of now. Mingie is not a weakling, and neither am I an invalid. Are you certain about your feeling for Clyde?"

"I—I don't know yet, Miss Rossie. Honestly, I don't."

And so my affairs stood on the very hot afternoon Mr. Lee came home early from the office. Leaving his car near the back door, he came in by way of the kitchen. "Well, now, how's our little cookie?" he hailed me, all aglow with his plans for the week end. "Throw out the pots and shut down your fires. We're off to the seashore!"

Before I could say anything, he had gone through the dining room and was calling to Miss Rossie. "Honey-y, let's get out the old bathing suit and pack up. I was in the doctor's office a while ago, and he said a few swims would do you good. So we're going down to the beach."

"All of us, daddy?" Edie cried eagerly.

"For three whole days!" her father said.

"Veanie too?"

"Yes, Veanie too!"

Edie ran to me to make sure I knew about it. I disappointed

her by not showing the enthusiasm she expected. "Why, Veanie, don't you want to go?"

"Yes, honey, but—"

Miss Rossie was at the door. "Is it Clyde?" she asked.

So I admitted it. Three whole days meant Friday, Saturday, and Sunday. On Saturday Clyde was returning from Collier City to stay over Sunday; then he would be away again for two weeks.

"You mustn't miss him, Veanie," Miss Rossie said.

I watched her leaning against the door for support. She would not admit to herself or to anyone how weak she still was. She would not think of herself.

"Miss Rossie, I'd like so much to go. I was just thinking, Miss Rossie, if it's all right, I'll go and have Mingie tell Clyde, when he comes, to run down to the beach to see me."

Her white hand—too white now—patted my arm. "Why of course, Veanie. Ask Mingie to send him down as soon as he gets in. Then after supper you can take him swimming."

So in my memory there remains a summer night, cooled by the breezes blowing inshore above the rising tide. The moon, soft and bright, hangs over the waves, casting a shimmering lane of light far out in the gulf. The daytime odors of fish and seaweed are lost in the freshness of the night air. The day-time cries of children have given way to the silken sound of the waves and, behind us, the rustling of the palms.

Clyde and I sit close together on the beach. My fingers sieve the deep, dry sand. There is no one in this glorious, lonely night but ourselves.

"Veanie, let's get married. I've got a good job down there in Collier City. I'll take good care of you. Will you, Veanie?"

I keep on sieving the sand, and Clyde waits. He's not crude or cruel. He doesn't try to overpower me. That's one of the reasons I love him. And I do love him—more than a little.

Enough? I ask myself. Enough?

Enough to be happy separated again from Mingie and now also from her boys who mean so much to me? Enough to leave Miss Rossie while she is still not herself? And, more selfishly, enough to give up my dream—a foolish dream, perhaps, but all the more precious for that—of college?

Miss Rossie had always made a great point of the importance of education. Yet she wanted me to be happily married, too. She had left me no doubt that the result of Mingie's marriage had not made her question the rightness of her original decision in regard to Mingie and Sam. Hadn't Mingie two fine little sons? And might not the marriage itself have worked out successfully—if it hadn't been for me?

Miss Rossie had never said it; she had never reproached or blamed me after Mingie and Sam had separated. But I knew how she felt. And I knew how she felt about Clyde and me. As in Mingie's case, she wanted me to decide for myself. I must be certain. With Mingie's example before me—

I didn't debate it coolly like that. I couldn't have, sitting so close to Clyde. I wanted to throw myself into his arms. How hard my heart was beating!

I edged away a little before I faced him. "Clyde," I said. "Clyde—" I had to draw further away.

"I—I can't; not just now, I can't marry you."

And now he had me in his arms, but I'd said it. I'd told him. I'd had the strength to say it, and that had been the hardest part.

"Why, Veanie? Veanie, you're crying!"

"Because I love you. But you'll have to wait for me—"

"I didn't tell you, Veanie, but after I get back to Collier City I'm being sent up north—going with my boss man—to New Jersey."

"For how long?"

"I don't know. Mr. Mason said that if I want—that's if we want. Veanie, if you marry me—I can keep the year-round job up there at his summer home. Wouldn't you like it north, Veanie?"

North! North where so many of us went, so many of my friends even from as small a place as our colored town. They never came back home. Up there they could ride in the same seats in trains and buses that white folks used, even sit beside them. The white people's stores were their stores too. Most places up north, the colored went to the same public schools with the white. There were more jobs to be had, and at better wages. There was no "Jim Crow"—but all the same, there was plenty of prejudice and discrimination. Letters came back to our colored town from up north. They told of good, but of bad too.

But in all the letters and in all the talk about better conditions in the North, I'd not had a hint of a white person showing to anyone up there a love to compare with Miss Rossie's for Mingie and me.

I didn't think this out at that moment, crying in Clyde's arms. I didn't have to. I just knew that there was no one anywhere in the world like Miss Rossie, and that I wasn't ready to leave her, not yet.

Hours after he had gone and I was in bed, I lay awake. The tears kept coming. I stopped them and they came again. I didn't hear the door open, but there, standing by my bed, was Miss Rossie.

I sat up. "Oh—I didn't mean to disturb you."

"But you didn't, Veanie. I wasn't sleeping and I thought I heard you." She came in, closing the door behind her. She sat on my bed. "Did you quarrel?"

"No, no, ma'am."

"Then what's wrong, honey?"

"He's gone, Miss Rossie."

"Gone? Why?"

"He has an offer of a job up north and he asked me to marry him and go with him. I told him I couldn't."

"Didn't you want to?"

"No, Miss Rossie; not now—not until you're all well, and I've finished school, and—" My voice trailed off.

"You told him no?"

"Yes, ma'am."

"Veanie, dear, those are not good reasons—if you love him."

She stood now, looking down at me; and how clearly I see her in the dim light of the bedside lamp. In front of the green-curtained window and above the pale-rose nightgown, her skin seemed a deep rose. Her eyes were sleepy and so soft—a lovely and loving blue. And I knew it wasn't because she was sick that I couldn't leave her, and it wasn't because of school. It was because where she was, the world was better for Mingie and her boys—and for me. It was beautiful and it was safe.

"Maybe he'll come back one day, Miss Rossie; and then I'll marry him."

"Nobody but you can know what you should do, Veanie, and what you want to do." She put out the lamp. "Good night, Veanie."

That was the night I bound myself to get to college.

I 7

I THOUGHT it would be hard to tell Mingie of my dream of college. She might feel that I wanted to desert her, leave her behind while I went up and out into the world. I was still haunted by a feeling of guilt: it was Mingie who'd found Miss Rossie; it was Mingie who should have stayed with her while I went to work for Mrs. Porter. If Mingie had stayed with Miss Rossie, everything would be different; we would be going to college together.

It was the old sore spot; and it was the old Mingie that was in my mind. But if I had been growing, so had my twin, and in her own way. Mingie had always been motherly. She had mothered me when we were little, and now the ache and doubts over leaving Sam had all but disappeared in her joy and care of her two sons and of our old house and little garden. Our house shone inside and out; the garden was blooming, and so were Teddy and Timmy—and so was Mingie.

"Oh, Veanie! College! I knew you'd get there. I've known

it all the time—or just about. You're going to be a teacher."

I hadn't got around yet to telling her that, but of course she'd know it! I had three pupils—Sonny Boy, Timmy, and Ted—who hardly knew I was teaching them; they were just playing with old Veanie. With Edie, my first and oldest pupil, it was now a regular thing for her to come to Veanie with her lessons. That was fun for both of us. Ever since Edie had said, showing me her report card, "We're smart—aren't we, Veanie?" and I had replied, "Yes, and we're going to get even smarter," we had joined in a little conspiracy. We were working together to get smarter and smarter. Sometimes I would find Edie trying to teach Sonny Boy. "Oh," she would say, losing patience, "you're just not smart—not like me and Veanie!"

Mingie, always practical, sat down at once to make plans. We talked for hours, for days. Never had we been so close together as now, planning a separation.

First I must finish high school, working part time for Miss Rossie. Then I would work for her full time for a year, saving every cent I could. Mingie would help with careful budgeting. We had an argument about that. I insisted there must be no sacrifices; Timmy and Teddy must come first. "And you too, Mingie. Plenty to eat and nice dresses—" I looked at my glowing twin. "Oh, Mingie, you're so pretty!" We hugged, and then we had to hug the little boys too, who weren't going to be left out when hugs were going around.

We knew, of course, that no matter how hard we both worked at it, we wouldn't be able to save up enough money to see me through. I'd have to get a job at college. I wasn't afraid of that, but a new worry was born that I kept to myself. It would have to be a good job. It would have to pay well enough so that I wouldn't be a drain on Mingie.

When I left, Mingie would support herself and the boys

by taking my place with Mrs. Lee. Aunt Tiller, who was obliged to stay home more and more, would look after Ted and Timmy while Mingie was at work. On days she couldn't, Mingie could take the boys with her to Mrs. Lee's.

We didn't ask Miss Rossie about it. There was still plenty of time and there was so much to think about and work out. When the time came, we would lay before her a plan complete in just about every detail, and she would do everything she could to help us, as always. There was only one thing that still troubled me. "Mingie," I said hesitantly, "how about school—I mean, for you. You'll be wanting to go back, won't you?"

"Veanie, honey, don't you worry about that. I will—some day. I'll be coming along right behind you. Just you wait and see."

In the months that followed I sometimes had to pinch myself. No, I wasn't dreaming. I'd had a dream, I'd taken it to Mingie, and it was a dream no longer but a clear and practical plan. What was more, the old sore spot had disappeared.

I myself all but wrecked any chance I had of carrying through the great plan.

One evening, on my way home from work, I saw three women some distance ahead of me and noticed that they turned their heads, frequently, to glance back at me. After crossing the railroad tracks, I was near enough to recognize them as the mothers of three of my classmates.

They stopped and stood at the side of the path to let me pass them. I greeted them each by name, politely. But there was nothing polite—and certainly nothing friendly—in their stares. One of them muttered a grudging good-evenin'. The other two didn't say anything at all.

I was too sensitive, Miss Rossie had often told me, too

quick to take offense. She had warned me against that; my temper might get me into trouble.

Having let me pass, the three women now were following me close enough so that I heard—as I had no doubt they meant me to hear—what they were saying.

"Yeah; it's true—somebody seen 'er with Liza's husban'. She ain' nothin'."

"Yeah, nothin' but a slut—runnin' roun' with another woman's man. The day ain' got but one eye, the night got a thousan'. She better learn it."

"Look at 'er—goin' long there with 'er head high in the air like she own the whole worl' and ev'ything in it. That white woman got 'er thinking she so good—her and that sister of hers that done runned off and had them babies and come luggin' 'em back. They bastards. That's what they is.

Then the second round started. "We oughta have 'er put outa school. She ain' fit to 'soshate with our girls. An' they give 'er all them prizes! The Sunday school gonna know 'bout this."

I was hurt and angry, but more puzzled. Liza's husband? I knew two Lizas who were married.

Then I recollected that long ago, back in January—New Year's night when I'd attended a watch meeting at the church—the husband of one of the Lizas, whose road home was almost the same as mine, had gone a little out of his way to see me through a very dark area on that winter night; and a couple of weeks ago, he'd shown me the same courtesy after another night service. He was a fine Christian man and he accompanied me in such a gentlemanly manner, on both occasions, that he hadn't come to my mind as one who could possibly cause scandalous talk. But they must mean him and, as I realized it, I became madder and madder at the three

188

women behind me and the vicious gossip that started such a lie about me and "Liza's husband."

On top of that was the cruel old lie about Mingie and her children. Nobody had flung that about for months, and along with it was another slap at Mrs. Lee for what she did for us.

I was furious. I kept control of myself, but beads of perspiration started out as I thrust through the thick grass between the path and the ditch. I was about to jump over when one of my tormentors yelled: "Look at that banged-up arm. I guess he done beat 'er up or somethin'."

I had a bandage on my right arm—strips of white gauze which Mrs. Lee had carefully applied to protect the burn I had received while carelessly reaching into the oven for a pan of biscuits. I wanted to tell them and shame them, but I knew they'd never shame. I wanted to strike them and curse them. But I went on home.

Mingie saw the state I was in. I told her what the women had said about me and how they'd referred to Miss Rossie. I didn't tell Mingie how they'd warmed over the old, cold lies about herself. But I might as well have told her; she soon heard it all.

For those tongues didn't stop, and others joined in spreading the scandals of Mingie and Veanie Bennett.

They all could remember us when we were miserable and pitiful—just about the most unfortunate family anywhere around. With Mrs. Lee's help, we'd lifted ourselves out of the palmetto scrub, and that alone was enough to make us a target for their tongues. I knew that some people found joy—the meanest of joys, yet a joy—in tearing others down; but that didn't prevent it from almost maddening me. But what could we do about it?

Mingie endured it better than I; she always had more courage. But Mingie didn't have to go to school and mix with people. Soon it got so bad that I couldn't; I took to staying home and going to Mrs. Lee's at the same late afternoon hour as when I'd attended my classes. All the while, I brooded over who had started the new lies and restarted the old ones. Somebody had, and I wanted to know who it was.

I could conceal from Miss Rossie that I'd dropped out of school, but I couldn't hide it from Aunt Tiller. It was not long before she came over to investigate.

I went into the back room as she hobbled into our yard. Mingie admitted her, and she limped to the brown rocking chair and plumped down. "Where Veanie?"

Mingie told her.

"She ain' sick?"

"No, she's all right."

"How she doin' in school? It done been goin' on a week now—ain' it?—that Veanie ain' been at school."

"No—no, ma'am, Aunt Tiller; she hasn't," Mingie admitted.

"You know, I been lookin' over here ev'y day an' thought I ain' seen that gal set foot outa this house nary mornin'."

Mingie said that she'd been trying to get me to go back to school, but I wouldn't while there was so much talk going around.

"Well, looka here, chile; course I hear that talk and I c'n tell you who-le lots 'bout it. Don' ne-va trus' your closes' frien'. I know, firs' han', jus' where it come from." And then Aunt Tiller named a girl whom I'd always considered one of my best friends.

"She's the one, Aunt Tiller?" Mingie cried, her voice strong and angry.

"Jes' as sho' as um settin' in this here chair."

I almost burst into the other room to question Aunt Tiller, but Mingie was doing so well that I stayed where I was and listened; however, Aunt Tiller knew nothing more. "Now, don' tell nobody I tol' you, Mingie. I don' want no trouble, but I thought y'all oughta know who is ya frien' an' who ain't."

Hurt as I had been before, I felt twice as injured now and more than twice as angry. Through the rest of the day, Mingie and I discussed what we ought to do.

I wanted to go to the girl and have it out with her, but Mingie was against that. "What would Miss Rossie say if she found out you were in a fight?"

"Miss Rossie'll never know," I asserted.

"You'll get in more trouble—real trouble, Veanie—and then she'll have to know," Mingie said sensibly. "How'll you get out of it without her?" And she urged: "Go on back to school, Veanie, and let this thing take care of itself. Hiding in the house isn't helping it."

Mingie got me to agree not to go to the girl and I didn't. What I did was worse and far more foolish.

At the usual hour, I went to Mrs. Lee's. Frequently, as I went about my chores, I saw her looking at me with a questioning expression. She asked me outright what was troubling me, and I denied that anything was. When I returned home, Mingie knew I was planning something and she tried to make me tell her what it was. I wouldn't, and that night I waited until I was sure she was asleep before I got paper and pencil and started my letter. By that time, I had it all planned in my mind—a cold, controlled, biting letter. But after I began writing and seeing the words on paper, I became angrier and more reckless. It was no more than that girl deserved—I told myself—to learn how low and rotten she was. So after I'd filled a page, I filled another and another; with each one, I became more abusive, more profane, more insulting. To this day I'm haunted by some of those penciled words of mine. That night I must have been near what they call berserk.

I folded the pages into an envelope, addressed it, and plastered on enough stamps to make sure it would be delivered. Then I put on a dress and my crepe-bottomed oxfords so as to make no noise as I crept out of the house and to the nearest mailbox.

After I'd dropped my letter in, the tension began to leave me. Cooler thoughts came, and before I reached home I was regreting some of the things I'd put on paper. But it was too late now.

I was careful entering the house but I woke up Mingie.

"Veanie?"

"Yes, Mingie."

"Where've you been? What you been doing?"

"I went to the mailbox with a letter."

"What letter?" my sister demanded.

"One I just wrote."

"To who?"

"To *her*," I told Mingie.

"Veanie! What was in it?"

"Everything—everything I wanted to say to her!" I said defiantly.

"Everything bad?"

"Yes—everything bad," I admitted. "And it's gone now, Mingie. It's in the mailbox. You can't get it back and I can't."

"Veanie! You wish you could get it back?"

"Some of it. Oh, Mingie!" I was wretched.

My letter was delivered—and brought to the attention of the postmaster. He brought it to me.

"Did you write this?"

"Yes, sir. I wrote it."

"And this is your signature signed here? This *is* your signature?" he had to ask again. I was trembling so that my own name blurred before me.

"Yes, sir," I finally managed.

He sighed. "Can you tell me how you could think up and write such foul language as this, put stamps on it, and send it through the United States mail?"

"Yes, sir. I was—"

"Do you know what the penalty is for such a thing? How old are you?"

"I'm seven—ah—sixteen."

"This woman you wrote this letter to said you were twenty-five."

"No, sir. I'm not."

He turned and went down the steps. "You come out here. Let me show you something, read you the law on this."

I followed him to his car and stood with my hand on it for support, watching him as he sat just inside the door, reached over, and tugged a huge black book to his lap. He thumbed through it, found the page he wanted, took out his glasses, and read, clearly and slowly, a long passage ending with "five thousand dollars and/or five years in prison." Then he looked at me. "That's it. Didn't you know that by writing such a letter and mailing it you were committing a serious Federal offense?"

I have no idea what I answered but I can still feel the fear that seized me. He asked me several other things, among them whether I went to school. I told him I was in my senior year in high school. "Will I have to go to prison?" I asked him.

"What to do in your case, I don't know," he said and without another word he drove away.

I stood rooted, staring after him. Mingie had been at the window, watching. She came out and I walked slowly to meet her. "Veanie, what all did he say?"

"H-he said five thousand dollars or five years in jail; so I guess I'll go to jail."

"Oh, Veanie, you've got to tell Miss Rossie. You've just got to!"

I realized that and was overwhelmed by shame. "You tell her, Mingie. Please, Mingie."

"All right. You mind the children and I'll go right now."

It didn't seem to me that I was fit to be minding children; I was too bad. But Mingie left, running.

I cowered in the house with the children. At last I saw the blue Pontiac, which told me that once more Miss Rossie had come, as so many times before—never, never failing me when I was in great trouble . . . after the hurricane, when Papa was dying, after the lynching, and through the pneumonia. My trouble today was different from any of those. I had committed a crime! I remembered the first time she'd come, bringing Mingie home with food for us all on that marvelous day Mingie found her. I'd been ashamed to show myself. Now I was much more ashamed. I'd not been to blame for my shame of that other day; for today's, I could blame only myself.

So, like long ago, I watched the car stop and Mingie jump out. I watched Miss Rossie step to the ground. She walked a little more swiftly than her usual pace.

Like long ago, I hid in the back room.

"Veanie," I heard Mingie call, "here's Miss Rossie."

I didn't reply.

Mrs. Lee came into the house. "Where are you, Veanie?"

Timmy ran to her. "Hey, Miss Rossie! Did you bring Sonny? Veanie's back there. She been crying an awful lot."

"No, Timmy, I didn't bring Sonny Boy today," I heard Mrs. Lee say and I knew she was patting Timmy's round little cheek. She came into the bedroom where I was sitting with my head bowed on the window sill. I began crying again.

"Oh, Miss Rossie, Miss Rossie! Please, ma'am, forgive me. I was too mad. I won't ever do anything like that again. . . . Miss Rossie—?"

"What, Veanie?"

"Will I have to go to jail?"

I was looking up at her now. Her face was thoughtful but it was kind. She didn't despise me! I wondered whether, while driving here, she'd counted—as I had—the years she'd been caring for us and how, whenever things were very bad, she'd come. Eight years. After all she'd done for me through eight years, I might have to go to jail!

"I know the postmaster quite well and I think I can go up and talk with him about it, Veanie," she said in her calm way. "He's very kind and considerate. Maybe he will let you off with a good warning."

"Oh, Miss Rossie, do you think he will?"

"I'll tell him, Veanie, how unlike you that letter is; and about your exceptionally good school record. But Veanie, why didn't you tell me that you weren't going to school?"

"I couldn't."

"That's no answer, honey. We all have to do many things it seems we can't do. You must return to your classes—though you've made it much harder for yourself, I know."

But how could I go back, after what I had done? Why, everyone would know. How could I face my teachers and classmates? How could I even walk down the road holding my head up?

"Veanie," Miss Rossie said, "you're planning to go to college. Mingie has told me about it. I want to see you carry out your plan. It's a good one and I'm very pleased about it."

College! How far away that seemed now! One had to be worthy of such an ambition, and I had proved myself unworthy. I had shrunk down to the ragged, savage little girl of the palmetto scrub.

"Veanie, you do want to go to college, don't you?"

"Yes, ma'am," I said hopelessly.

"Well, how do you expect to get there if you don't finish high school?"

"But Miss Rossie, you haven't seen that letter yet. When you do, you—you'll hate me!"

"Will I?" And through my tears I saw that she was smiling. "Will I, now, Veanie?" It was a gently teasing smile. Why, she was laughing at me for having such a crazy notion!

I jumped up. "Oh, Miss Rossie, I will! I mean, I'll go right back to school—if I don't have to go to jail."

18

AS A MINOR I could not be penalized for what I had done, but the seriousness of my offense was not overlooked. I went to the postmaster and was grateful for his reprimand and warning. Now, with humility and determination, I could go on.

I went back to school.

It was hard. I could not be angry at the silent stares, the whispers, the snickers; I had deserved them. And in a way, they were good for me. They acted as a goad. I worked as I never had before. Soon I was high above the shying-away students and the snigglers. And little by little, I was spoken to, I was invited places, I had friends again. At first I was astonished to find that some of them were full of respect and admiration, not for my school work, but for my "crime"—for the very foulness of the letter I had written. That, I felt, was very wrong. And of course it was. But when I told Mingie about it, she began to laugh. She looked at my indignant face and laughed more than ever. The episode did have its funny aspects, I suppose, but I could never bring myself to laugh at it.

I graduated with the second highest grades of the twenty-two seniors and was made salutatorian of the class. For a little ship done in polychrome clay and for a landscape drawing, I won two first prizes at the county fair. But now, for a year, my schooldays were over. I was working full time for Miss Rossie and saving every cent I could for college.

The week before Christmas, Mingie and I counted our savings on the kitchen table: ninety-three dollars and forty cents.

"I'll take some out for a present for you," I said to Mingie.

"You can't"—Mingie reached out and grabbed my wrist —"because then you'd have to let me take some out for you."

"Anyway, for the children."

"No! We'd go on and on, and pretty soon there wouldn't be anything left. Miss Rossie will have presents for Ted and Timmy; and she always gives us such a nice dinner."

"Oh, Mingie, we've just got to have presents for Miss Rossie—and Edie—and Sonny Boy—and—"

"Veanie, we're not going to touch a penny of it! You know Miss Rossie wouldn't stand for it. The best way is to do extra little things for her."

I did one extra thing that was very hard. Of course, I did it for myself as well; but nothing could have pleased Miss Rossie more. I went to the girl to whom I'd written my awful letter and we made up. I'd never had proof that she had started those stories about me; only Aunt Tiller's word. Almost crying, the girl denied she'd had anything to do with the affair, and so we had no trouble forgiving each other. She had an unusually good voice, and I invited her to join a little group I was taking to sing carols at Mrs. Lee's. She came early, as we planned, and that was how we told Miss Rossie.

Every year after Christmas, Northerners came down, renting the beach houses and giving parties. They lived apart from the rest of the town and were considered strange. They dressed and walked differently, and their voices sounded hard and flat on Southern ears. But they gave work to many people of colored town, and sometimes a colored boy or girl would go north with them.

Some were very rich and particular people who wanted things just right when they entertained. This year Miss Rossie gave Mingie and me new organdy aprons and caps done up nice and stiff and encouraged us to accept a night's work now and then, if we could. She'd instructed us so well that Mingie and I each would sometimes earn five dollars for one night, serving at a big party. We had offers from one family after another to go back home with them. We were still living in slavery down here, they'd say; we'd make much more money and be better treated, north.

"Don't you ever tell Miss Rossie about what that Chicago woman says she'd pay," I cautioned Mingie. "I'm staying right her and I don't want Miss Rossie's feelings hurt."

Mingie laughed at me. "Miss Rossie isn't that easily hurt. Why, she'd *help* you to go if you wanted to and thought you'd be better off, Veanie."

"But I wouldn't. I don't believe I'd be better off."

"Well, if you want to go and find out—and you hit 'rough water,' like Aunt Tiller says, and come 'floatin' back,' you wouldn't have to worry. Miss Rossie would be just the same."

The Northerners' big tips increased my savings. Yet when fall came, I was still far short of the minimum I had to have in order to start college. Miss Rossie asked me about it. I told her what I had and that I needed seventy-five dollars more.

"Mr. Lee will have to decide what to do about that," Miss Rossie said. "Tell him, Veanie."

I'd never had to ask anything of Mr. Lee. Whenever Mingie or I had needed anything, like the schoolbooks, Miss Rossie had asked him for us. It was different now. If I was to go away to college, I'd be facing the world by myself, without Mingie—who'd usually acted first for the two of us—and without Miss Rossie to shield me. It was going to be harder, much harder, for me to ask a loan from him than from her; and, having told me to ask for it myself, she wouldn't help me by speaking about it to him first.

For some days, in the morning and when Mr. Lee came home for lunch and in the evening, I'd be staring at him or trying to tiptoe around him, studying him and my problem. One afternoon I caught him looking at me in a puzzled kind of way. "Is it a game?" he asked.

Edie was behind me. She had followed me from the kitchen to the living room, in the same wary way I had walked and had the same look on her face I had on mine—the concentrated studying look of her lessons.

"It's a game!" Mr. Lee decided.

"No—I mean—yes, sir!" I fled.

I decided the best time to approach him was when he came home for lunch. He was nearly always light and happy at noon; often in the evening he was tired.

On the day I had fixed upon, he came almost waltzing in the front door, put his arms about Miss Rossie and kissed her, made the children squeal with delight, and on his way to the bathroom called to me, in the kitchen: "Cookie, what's good to eat today? I'm hungry as a bear, so put it on."

I had everything ready, including my organdy apron and cap. They had hardly got into their chairs when I put bowls of soup before each one. They were hardly finished when I whisked the bowls away. I brought in pork roast, green peas, tomato salad, cornbread. I'd taken particular pains to roast the pork just right—it was Mr. Lee's favorite.

As I was removing his plate, he said with a happy sigh: "All right, now, cookie; what's next?"

"Ice cream, Mr. Lee."

"Bring it on. I'm still starving."

I knew his favorite was strawberry, and this time I had fresh strawberries spread thickly on top. I brought in Mr. Lee's the last so that if he said no to the loan I wouldn't be coming back to the table with a sad face. The helping I gave him was enormous. When I set it before Mr. Lee, Sonny Boy opened his eyes wide. "Look! Look how much Daddy's got! Veanie," he said reproachfully, "you gave him more than me!"

"And more than me, too!" Edie exclaimed.

Mr. Lee said in mock alarm: "Veanie, what have I done to deserve this?"

Now was the time—and I was suddenly so embarrassed that I couldn't speak or even move. I just stood there.

And Miss Rossie couldn't help herself. She couldn't let me suffer, not even a little bit. She said to Mr. Lee: "Maybe it's because Veanie wants you to do her a little favor, honey. How about it, Veanie?"

How much easier that made it for me! But it was hard all the same. "Yes, sir, Mr. Lee, I do want to ask you, please, sir. I want to ask to borrow some money for my college fees and I want to ask if I may work in the summer to pay it back.

"Ah hah—so that's it! She's been bribing me with roast pork and strawberry ice cream!" Then he said more seriously: "How much is it, Veanie?"

"Sir, it's—" But the sum was enormous, far more enormous than the dish of strawberry ice cream! I got it out: "Seventy-five dollars, Mr. Lee."

Surprised, he looked at Miss Rossie. "A *little* favor, you said?" Then his eyes rose to mine. "Why, that's a lot of money, Veanie. When will you have to have it?"

"About—" I began. But I couldn't go on. It had been altogether too much to ask, even to think of asking. I wanted to sink down through the floor.

Miss Rossie helped me again. "Oh, she won't need it before about three weeks from now, dear."

"We'll see, Veanie," said Mr. Lee, and somehow I stumbled back to the kitchen.

A few days later when I arrived at the house Mr. Lee had already gone. Miss Rossie was still in bed. She heard the door open and close and called from the bedroom, "Is that you, Veanie?"

"Yes, ma'am; it's me, Miss Rossie. Are you up?"

"No. I'm lazy this morning. Come on in."

I went to her swiftly. "How are you feeling, Miss Rossie?"

"Fine." She sat up. "Look over on the dressing table. There's something for you. Right there on the edge."

It was a large envelope. In it was a letter of recommendation from Mr. Lee to help me in getting a job at college, and there was a check for seventy-five dollars.

Tallahassee. The railroad station was much farther from the school than I had thought it would be. I had a turtle-backed truck and a suitcase and was wondering what to do about them when a cab driver come over. "Taxi, lady? To the college?" He was picking up my luggage.

"How much to the college?" I asked.

"One dollar, ma'am—and twenty-five cents for your baggage."

I had put aside, in my purse, three dollars and forty-seven cents. That would have to do for my personal expenses until

I found a job. Mr. Lee's seventy-five dollars and all my savings were going to tuition and college costs. I just couldn't afford that taxi.

To my surprise and relief another way was offered. Two young men approached, each pushing a huge, clumsy wheelbarrow. They were racing each other, laughing. "Dray for hire!" breathlessly announced the one who reached me first.

"You take luggage to the campus?" I asked.

"Yeah. You've got two pieces. That'll be fifty cents."

I fished out a half dollar. He loaded my luggage and hurried to a girl standing alone with three suitcases, one very worn and with a rope around it. She paid him and he thrust on to a bashful-faced boy with a wooden box and a big, battered gripsack.

As we walked along behind the wheelbarrow, I noticed that that the dress of the girl who was walking beside me was old and faded, though clean. Her shoes were worn; her hat was far from new. The bashful boy's suit had faded from its original navy blue and had worn thin and shiny. I had been afraid that I would be conspicuous among the students for poverty. Plainly, other students had less than I.

The wheelbarrow boy stopped under a tall eucalyptus tree and sat down on an exposed root to rest. We stood around him.

"Well, let's all get acquainted," he suggested, wiping the sweat from his face. "What's your name, fellow?"

"Lester Perkins." Lester loosened up a little and removed his hat. "What's yours?"

"Joe—Joe Mickens."

"My name is Ella Jones," the girl said.

"Mine is Veanie Bennett." I felt good. How friendly everyone was!

"You're all freshmen?" Joe asked.

"Yes," we said together.

A broad smile spread over Joe's good-natured face. "You're dogs. I'm a junior and shouldn't be hauling stuff for dogs, but I need the money. Got to scrape every penny to see me through this term. The job they gave me pays only half my board and room. The rest I have to hustle up the best I can. Girls get an easier break—they get soft jobs."

My worry about a job was at the top of my mind. I had mailed Mr. Lee's letter of recommendation to the employment bureau along with my request for a job that wouldn't interfere with my classes. A courteous reply had come back, assuring me that I could get work. But what kind and at what pay? Nothing was said about that.

I asked Joe, "What are some of the jobs for girls?"

"Well, I've seen some working down in the training school. Some clean offices, some carry mail, some take care of the lobbies and other places in the hospital. A lot of 'em wait table in the dining hall. Now, the last one is the hardest but it pays the most, if you can take it—especially a dog." He laughed and shook his head. "It's heavy work anyway, and the upper classmen make it harder for doggies. . . ."

Lester asked: "How about me? What can I find?"

"Let's see—being a dog, you might get on at the dairy, or janitoring in the Ag building."

Joe got up. "Say, dog," he addressed Lester with a superior air, "you better roll this thing some now." He weakened. "You don't have to, fellow—but it'll save you a lot of skin in the end. We're rough on dogs who don't mind upper classmen."

So Lester took a turn but Joe, the good-hearted, soon resumed his job. At the campus he left my luggage and Ella's at one "dog house"—freshman dormitory—and went off with Lester to the other "dog house."

Following Joe's advice, Ella and I went at once to the office of the dean of women, where we found there was just one double room unassigned in the freshman women's dormitory.

In quick succession, we registered, paid our first month's room and board, and settled into our room. Then I went to the office of the director of student labor. Introducing myself, I gave the director the letter I had received in answer to my application.

He was cordial. "Oh, yes. That was an impressive letter from your employer you sent us, Miss Bennett. I think we have something for you."

He twirled in his swivel chair and riffled through his files. Explaining the jobs available, he confirmed what Joe had said—the best-paying was a job as waitress in the dining hall.

"I'll take waiting on table," I said.

"All right. You may start this evening at supper."

So at supper that night, only a little more than two hours after my arrival at the college, the fun began.

I reported at the dining hall, took up one of the huge aluminum trays, loaded it, and carried it to the long table assigned to me. It was a senior table. The ten students around it eyed me, but they appeared only aloof as I set the heavy tray on the nearby rack. I had placed all the dishes before the diners, except the one holding the butter, when the student at the head of the table—a tall, robust young woman—raised her arm and beckoned me. When I came near, she waved me off. "Go back, dog, and get the beef grease."

"Beef grease? Where? What's that?"

"Better find out, dog, and quick!" she snapped.

"Well, I don't know what you're talking about," I retorted with rising temper. And that was just what she, and the others, wanted.

"Now, little doggie, is your time to learn," one of them said. Getting up, she took possession of the plate of butter which I had left at the other end of the table. "Now keep very still, doggie. This isn't going to hurt you any—just your pride." She had dug into the butter and now came toward me with a great gob of it in her hand.

I retreated, but another girl ran behind me and held my arms in back. While I struggled, the first girl smeared my face with butter, and then doused me with water from the table glasses. There were shouts of laughter, not only from my table but from all over the room. Other doggies were getting the same kind of treatment.

As the hazing continued, it took the best within me to keep from attacking my tormentors. How I wanted to scratch those grinning faces! In spite of Joe's warning, I wasn't prepared for the hurt and humiliation. With them came a sort of aching bewilderment. Why did they want to do it? How could they enjoy it? Most of them must have worked as hard as I had, or harder, and prepared and saved as long, in order to get here. When they arrived, they must have felt the same sense of achievement—triumph—that I had been feeling only a few minutes before. And now they were destroying all that in me.

In the kitchen I cleaned my face and tried to dry out my hair. It had kinked and looked like a rat's nest. I'd paid a dollar to have it straightened and curled a little at the ends. One of my hard-earned dollars wasted.

Pain and misery overwhelmed me. It was much more than a dollar hair-do that had vanished. An old dream had come true at last, and the truth was dreadful. The world was cruel and frightening, and there was no place here to run away and hide and wait for Miss Rossie to come and fix things. Miss Rossie. . . . I would go home. I'd hit rough water; I'd float back and Miss Rossie would be just the same. Tomorrow. Tomorrow I'd take the train and go right home, where everything was safe.

On my way to the dormitory I met Ella coming from her

work as janitress in the elementary training school building. I asked her about her job, and she was jubilant about it. "And how about yours, Veanie?"

I told her, but didn't say I was going home. I added: "They said that at breakfast tomorrow they're going to do something else to me. Did they get to you?"

"No. Nobody bothered me at all. Why, there wasn't even anybody there."

I wished I'd taken her job instead of the one I had. Maybe I could still change. Considering that, I said to myself: "I needn't ever tell Miss Rossie; she'll never know."

But now with the thought of Miss Rossie came something else, something she'd once said to me:

"When you're climbing a hill, Veanie, keep on to the top. It's always easy to stop and very much easier to descend. But you give up when you do, and then it's twice as hard just to regain the ground you've lost."

Right there, walking to the dormitory with Ella, I knew I wasn't going to run home and hide; and I decided to keep my job, see it through. To make doubly sure, as soon as I got back to our room, I sat down and wrote two letters—one to Mingie and the other to Miss Rossie. I told each of them I'd had been given a good room and found a nice roommate—and arrived, had been lucky to have landed the best-paying job open to a freshman girl.

When I'd mailed the letters, my decision was sealed; I wouldn't go back on it, no matter what. All the same, I lay awake a long while that night, still hurt and angry, and apprehensive over the "something else" I would have to endure tomorrow morning.

THE "something else" turned out to be running—or rather, walking—a gauntlet of sophomores, juniors, and seniors, each armed with a wooden paddle or a hose. The paddles hurt. The hoses spurted water into my face. And how they laughed, those hateful girls! Grimly determined, I took it all, laughing. There were tears in my eyes, but my face was wet anyway so no one could see that. . . . And at last it was over. This was the worst, and it was over. I was "in"—with only a year before me of "doggie baiting."

Hazing was an ugly game. But for the hazed it could be quite easily forgotten. There was no lasting humiliation in it; nothing to compare with my feelings over what happened when, a little later, a man I liked asked me for a date. He was a junior and one of the football heroes of the campus. I was elated. He was going to take me to a movie on Friday evening. It was *Imitation of Life*, as I'll always remember. I was to wait for him in the lobby of my dormitory. He would come for me at seven-thirty.

The next three days went by at the slowest snail's pace. At last it was Friday. I dressed in my very best—a silk frock that had been Miss Rossie's and that she had worn only a few times before giving it to me. It was a beautiful dress, and I knew she had paid a lot for it. I studied myself critically in the mirror. "Veanie Bennett," I told myself, "you'll do." I went down to where the other girls were waiting for their dates.

Promptly at seven-thirty, my date come in. Tall and elegant he stood in the center of the large room, looking at the couples assembling to go to the theater. The freshmen girls who had no escorts had already been sent out together by the matron.

Not once did my date's eyes reach me. There was something so deliberate about the evasion that I did not—could not—give him any sign. I just stood there, waiting. Then, hurriedly, an upper-class girl came through the side door and went straight over to him.

Gaily she said, "Did you think I was never coming? Sorry I'm late but I was at a Delta meeting. It just went on and on."

His eyes were all for her. "That's all right; we won't be late." And out they went, together.

I can still see him in his navy blue suit and her in her too cheaply pretty beige dress, as they went out.

I was in bed when Ella came in. "Veanie!" she called to me excitedly. "I didn't see you and your date. I was staring like mad to see you walk down that middle aisle."

I had to tell her. And then I turned my face to the wall.

He came to me some days later. The upper classmen, he said, had been jeering at him for having asked a doggie for a date. They had put pressure on him, telling him he was letting them down. What he'd done, he explained, wasn't really "personal"; it was just part of my "discipline." He had the nerve to propose another date, and I had the bitter satisfaction of turning him down flat.

Prejudice is many things. It's the strong bullying the weak, as when Mingie and I were ragged little girls. It's a pack hunting down one defenseless man, as in the lynching. It's the envious trying to pull down the envied, as in the lying scandals spread about Mingie and me back in colored town. It's the ungenerous yapping at the generous, as in the criticism by the new neighbor who complained about our playing the piano at Mrs. Lee's. And sometimes it's no more than senseless tradition, as upper classmen against freshmen in college.

Prejudice is not confined to race.

My experience with my first date made me turn down others. No, thank you; I wasn't going to let myself in for more "discipline."

My studies were all that mattered—that, and the letters from home. When I wrote Miss Rossie, back came a reply with never a long delay, full of warm concern for me. "Watch your health, Veanie; don't overwork." But I couldn't work hard enough. Miss Rossie and Mingie were back of me, two solid supports in a bleak world.

I was determined to make an average of B or higher in my grades. But if I succeeded, I would be eligible for a sorority. That was something to think about; it would mean an additional expense. Well, there was no "must" about it. I could turn down an invitation to join a sorority, if it came.

But suddenly I saw that I was "moping," as Miss Rossie would have said. I was bitter and feeling sorry for myself. I saw a gentle reproving smile on a beloved face. None of that, Veanie Bennett!

When the Christmas holidays came, I had to make up my mind whether to hang on to the seven dollars I'd saved or spend it going home.

Home. Home was Mingie and Timmy and Ted—Sonny

Boy, Edie, Mr. Lee—Miss Rossie. Miss Rossie had a place all by itself in my heart. It ached to see her again, to hear her. But Miss Rossie would see I wasn't really happy in college, and Mingie too. I couldn't keep anything from them. And at home Mingie would spend on me some of her money she was earning now. And Christmas presents—how could I come home without any? Last year I'd given nothing and had learned that it was very hard to receive and to be unable to give.

So I didn't go home.

Sad and sadder I became through the hurry and scurry of the homegoers. Suitcases bumped down the stairs. There was excited laughter and shouts of "Good-by! Merry Christmas!" Some of the students went off to the station in cabs. Others were picked up by friends with cars. But most of them relied on their own legs to get them to the station and Joe's wheelbarrow to trundle their baggage. So many of my college mates were as hard-pressed for money as I was. But I envied them all the same—they were going home for Christmas.

And now the dormitory was silent. I was alone.

To cheer myself up, I set to arranging on my bureau the bright-colored, home-smelling fruit from the box Miss Rossie had sent me. I heard footsteps in the hall and knew it was the day matron going about checking and locking the deserted rooms. She came to my door, found it closed, and rapped on it.

"Hello," she greeted me. "Are you staying?"

"Yes, ma'am."

She stepped in. "It's going to be pretty lonesome up here. Everyone else has gone from this floor. Would you like to move down to the floor below? There are a few other girls there who are staying."

"Thank you, Mrs. Shannon, but I'd just as soon stay up here."

"Where do you live?"

"Fort Myers."

"That's a long way, isn't it?"

"Yes, ma'am. It's way south, on the Gulf coast."

She admired the fruit and I invited her to have some. "Thank you," she said. "I'll have an orange."

But it wasn't an orange she picked up. "What's this? I've never seen one before."

"That's a sapodilla plum, they call it. It grows only in south Florida. It's a tropical fruit."

"And that's a mango, I know that at least." Mrs. Shannon indicated a red and yellow Hayden. "But I didn't know they grew so large."

Then she said, "Did your mother send you this beautiful fruit?"

The simple question distrubed me. It brought out an ardent longing that had been buried deep inside me for long years. I loved the word "mother" so much. If only mother were Miss Rossie! Childishly, in my loneliness, I made the make-believe come true for a moment, only for a moment:

"Yes, ma'am, Mrs. Shannon; my mother—"

But make-believe was lying and so I hurried to explain.

My attitude toward Miss Rossie was feudal—simply feudal—said the Straight Thinker.

I called her that to myself because she was always saying: "I'm just trying to think straight—as you can do if you care to. Of course, if you don't, I can't make you. . . ."

She was a senior, about twenty-five, small, soft-spoken, light-colored. She went about setting other students "straight," even doggies. She had a bigger curiosity—"interest in others," she called it—than I'd even seen. "Feudal" was her favorite word. Six letters, she'd say, described the South. The War

212

Between the States, she said, had ended chattel slavery but had scarcely shaken the feudal system.

She came to me to learn all about Miss Rossie, and I told her; I was so happy to talk about Miss Rossie. In fact, I talked about her just about all the time, to Ella and to other girls. Tales of Veanie Bennett and her Miss Rossie reached the ears of those high, rarefied beings, the seniors, and that's how it happened that the Straight Thinker came to me.

I was flattered by her visit. I chattered along as fast as my tongue would go.

The Straight Thinker kept nodding, as if in agreement. But she was only biding her time to get a word in, and when it came, it was "feudal," and then she couldn't be stopped. Yes, it was very nice what Mrs. Lee had done for me and Mingie. But I was grown up now and going to college, and it was time I began to think straight and see it for what it was—merely an instance of personal kindness without "social significance." There always had been instances of such kindness in every feudal society, she said, but they changed nothing. They didn't really attack the "social structure." What the South needed was new laws and enforcement of them. Isolated kindness that benefited a few individuals was of no "significance."

When the Straight Thinker had had her say and I was alone again, I found myself with Mrs. Lee's latest letter in my hand. My eyes fell upon its last words—

Devotedly,
Your Miss Rossie

"Devotedly."

I didn't think it out; I didn't have to. "Devotedly" and "your" Miss Rossie—that wasn't feudal. Why, it was no more feudal than a loving mother is "feudal" toward her children.

Was there no "social signifiance" in such a love? That was just plain silly!

Somehow, it seemed to me I had found the meaning of my life in Miss Rossie's "Devotedly." So the Straight Thinker gave me further incentive to work very hard. Yet, after the examinations in January, I found I had won only one A; there were two B's and two C's.

I went to work with renewed determination. But at the end of the second semester I'd only brought one C—in psychology— up to a B. I still hadn't improved my algebra, and I had only one A, as before. So again I had fallen short of making the honor roll.

I was ashamed. I was to go home for the summer, but how could I go home like this—a failure!

I wrote to Miss Rossie. She replied by return mail:

"We know you've done your best, Veanie. Never mind that C. Your grades are wonderful for a student who comes from a small town where education just can't be up to the high standards of a fine university. When you're a teacher yourself, maybe you'll help to change that. Come on home, honey. Sonny Boy said learn a lot of new stories for him. . . ."

It was a glorious homecoming. Mingie was at the station with Timmy and Ted. How big the boys had grown, and how lovely Mingie was! We all went straight to Mrs. Lee's.

Miss Rossie was waiting at the door. "Oh, Veanie, we're so glad you're home!" She hugged me and walked me with her arm about my waist to the dining room. "Mingie's serving but she'll sit with us anyway. This is a very special occasion. We haven't eaten yet. Mingie's hungry as a horse, waiting to eat with you."

Feudal?

I started working again at Mrs. Lee's the next morning. On Saturday my check was for eight dollars. I stared at it. There must be some mistake. Eight dollars was very high pay for a Negro maid in Florida in the early thirties.

"Miss Rossie," I began hesitantly, "did—didn't Mr. Lee take out on my loan?"

"Yes, he did, Veanie. He took out two dollars."

"Two? But, Miss Rossie, he's made a mistake. This check is for eight dollars."

She smiled. "No, it's all right, Veanie. You're earning ten dollars a week now."

Throughout the summer I worked for my princely wage while Mingie worked part time for Mrs. Porter. When I returned to college, a check was waiting for me. Mr. Lee, without having said a word, had forwarded fifty dollars more to help me through my sophomore year.

That year I made the honor roll.

20

IN MY JUNIOR YEAR I worked too hard. For a while I had three jobs at once and became exhausted. When I went home, my loss of weight worried Miss Rossie. "Veanie, are you sick? I believe you should stay home with Timmy and Ted for a while and rest up."

I said, "No, ma'am, Miss Rossie. Helping you here is resting."

Mingie fussed over me that summer, and so did Miss Rossie in her way. I had to drink milk and eat ice cream until I could hardly stand the sight of either. But at the end of that summer I weighed more than I ever had in my life. I looked like Mingie again; nobody could tell us apart except Miss Rossie.

As I was leaving for my senior year at college, Miss Rossie said: "Veanie, you're a young lady now. You've gained confidence in yourself."

My mind went back to the first day, the day she had come into our lives. I saw the shamed and frightened and half-savage little black girl, hiding from the strange white woman in the wretched room where Papa lay. And that little girl was in Miss Rossie's mind too; for, looking at me, her eyes filled with tears.

So did mine. I wanted to say "Thank you" for all the years between that day and this. But I couldn't. "Thank you" wasn't enough. There just weren't any words.

"It's all right," she said, as she had said that first day when she had seen Papa.

I was crying like a baby and her arms were around me. "It's all right, Veanie, honey. You've made me so happy!"

My senior year passed quickly. I had my studies better in hand. I worked with less strain and I had many friends. I met with success in other activities. I won a first prize, and also a second, in oratory. Two of my poems were published in the college newspaper, and I had a song and a dance in the talent show. On graduation day I stood second in line—next after the salutatorian—and as I was one of the two graduates with the highest average in the field of education, mine was one of the two envelopes containing a scholarship to Fisk University for postgraduate work.

I'd hoped—expected—that Mingie or Miss Rossie, or even both of them, would attend my graduation. But neither did. There was a lovely, heart-warming message of congratulation from Miss Rossie; that was all. When I got home, I learned why. Mingie was ill and Miss Rossie had kept it from me so as not to worry me. Miss Rossie had Mingie under her doctor's care, and Cindy—a friend of Mingie's and mine—temporarily had our place at Mrs. Lee's. Our place. . . .

It was frightening to find Mingie weak and helpless in bed, but she was already recovering. I looked after her and the two boys. But soon she was up and about, and then our place at Mrs. Lee's was mine again. Mine for what was left of the summer, and then not mine. For now I was to be a teacher. From the college I'd written the superintendent of the school Mingie and I had attended, applying for the first teaching position open.

Mr. and Mrs. Lee urged me to use the scholarship I had won to Fisk University. I reminded Mr. Lee that I still owed him money.

"Veanie," he said, "you know that arithmetic is your weak point."

"No, sir," I said a little indignantly; "algebra, not arithmetic."

He laughed and stopped teasing and told me to forget about the money; he and Mrs. Lee were making it their graduation present to me. I thanked them as best I could, and again they said I should use my scholarship. But I thought of Mingie. One day, she had promised, she would be going back to school. I must be ready to help her in case she needed help. So I kept to my decision to start teaching as soon as I could. Mr. Lee knew the superintendent of schools and spoke to him about me.

That was a happy summer, after Mingie got well. I had the promise that I'd be considered for the first position open. There was a lot of teasing of "Teacher," but I enjoyed that. There was playing and telling stories to Mingie's boys and Sonny, and ever so solemn, confidential talks with Edie, who was now a young lady. Mingie and I went out on dates once in a while, dressed alike and looking alike.

In the fall a teaching job was offered me. The place was an offshore island in the Gulf. It had a tourist hotel where several Negro families worked as janitors, cooks, waiters, and dishwashers. There were only seven children of school age, but another Negro family with a child was expected. That would make up the eight pupils required for setting up a school.

I boarded the boat for the island. When I arrived, I discovered there were no Negro car drivers, so I had to walk the two miles from the pier down a lonely shell road to the building to which I had been directed. It was an old, abandoned church. The paint on its boards was blistered; the windowpanes were broken. It had a ghostly look.

I had heard about this island and this church. When the hotel building was going on, a colored minister had come to start a church for the workmen. He'd built it mostly of left-over pieces of lumber. When it was done, a hurricane hit the island. One of the church members was killed that night, in the church, and no one had used the structure since. Now it was to be my home and my school.

My eyes shifted over the miles of yellow saw grass into the empty distance, and it seemed to me I was small again. I looked the other way to a dense orange grove two hundred or more yards distant and had a glimpse of a white house and an elderly white woman standing in the yard.

Cautiously I mounted the single wooden step of the church and went in. There were five, long, hard benches strewn, rather than placed, across the room, as the people had left them the night of the hurricane. And there was a pitiful, upset pulpit. Nothing else.

Behind the pulpit, a door led to a room about eight feet by ten. It was furnished with the wreck of an old piano, a rusty, two-burner oil stove on a chair, and a flat-padded cot. This was where I was to live.

I looked up. The shingles, battered by the seasonal storms, were torn apart, thin, cracked, or decayed so that bats and owls had established themselves under the roof. The rats that had escaped them had a home of their own in the hull of the piano; I could hear their squeaking and scurrying.

My dismay gave way to a sick feeling. Years ago I had hoped

—and believed—I had escaped such as this forever. Miss Rossie had made possible my escape.

Miss Rossie. . . . "Moping, Veanie?" My spirits rose. Here before me was work, and of the best kind. The least I could do was to attempt to give to others a little of what she had given Mingie and me. I put on my oldest dress—even that was too good right now—and began to clean and tidy my first school.

Darkness brought the screech and scuffle of the owls and the winging of the bats fluttering out into the night. Through the roof the stars twinkled. And here was morning, the sun—and seven eager black faces looking up at me.

Seven. There wasn't an eighth—the necessary eighth if the school was to be maintained. But I started teaching. The schooling—or lack of schooling—of no two of the seven children was the same. In a larger school they would have been in five or six different "grades." But many great men—and women—had made their start in a one-room country schoolhouse and in circumstances like these.

Each evening, after school, I walked a half mile or more home with the children and then on by myself, down the hot shell road toward the pier where I bought my necessities at the only store.

Often at night, lying on my cot watching the flutter of the bats and listening to the whistled cry of the marsh wrens, I weakened. I lifted myself and gazed out into the brilliant moonlight and watched the breeze ruffle the saw grass as if it were a lonely sea, and I wanted to be home—home with Mingie and her boys and with Sonny Boy, Edie, and Miss Rossie. But I'd written Miss Rossie of the splended chance I had here.

Yes, after my first day, I'd deliberately done that. I'd committed myself to stay and stick it out.

Besides, I'd committed myself to the children; for I'd had them scrubbing floors, taking out broken window glass, painting furniture, and hoeing weeds from the yard. The place had become almost presentable when, one afternoon, I looked up to see a long black sedan drive up from the direction of the ferry. The car stopped and the superintendent got out.

"Hello, Veanie!" he hailed me. "How are you making out?"

I was very glad to see him. "How are you, Mr. Randake? I'm doing all right, sir," I told him.

His eyes roved about at the improvements I had made. "I see you have things looking pretty good," he approved.

"Thank you, sir. It does look a little better. And I've got the schoolwork started, with some of the children reading and some—" I launched out on the classwork. He listened for a minute, nodded, smiled, and then shook his head and stopped me.

"What you've been doing is all right, Veanie!" he quickly and kindly reassured me. "But I see by your report that you still have only the seven pupils with whom you started. Is that correct?"

"It's correct, sir."

"By law, as you know, you must have eight to constitute a school."

"Oh, yes, sir; but somebody else is sure to move down here soon."

He shook his head, kindly as before. I realized this meant he'd come to close my school, and I was almost in panic. I hadn't guessed how much this work meant to me—and how much I wanted to stay with those seven children.

"Mr. Randake, sir, I hoped, when I saw you, you'd come to tell me I could go on here—and maybe have more repairs made and more equipment."

"I'm sorry, Veanie, but a regulation is a regulation. I must close you out here. I'm sending you over to Boca Grand Island for the rest of the term."

221

"Boca Grand?" I asked in surprise.

"Yes. A teacher there is going back to college to finish her work for a degree; so I have to replace her. That's a pretty nice school over there, with many more children. You'll like it there, Veanie."

I hated having to say good-by to my seven children. I had come to love them all. Now they must stop their schooling and go without—for how long? For the rest of their lives?

I did like it at Boca Grand, but the seven children I had left behind on the little island with the abandoned church, now again abandoned, haunted me. They still do. So often I've wondered what happened to them and thought of the difference it might have made to them if one more pupil had come to my school.

HOME AGAIN. In the fall, after Boca Grand and the summer vacation, I was appointed head of the English department of the high school from which I had graduated six years before. I was filled with joy, the quiet kind that sings in the heart.

Opening day. I dressed carefully to look neat and a little prim for my appearance before my first high school English class. It was a twelfth-grade group. I sat on the platform while they were assembling and was suddenly aware of familiar faces. Like Mingie, a number of students I'd gone to school with had dropped out for one reason or another; like Mingie, they came back if they could. Here before me were not a few young men and women I'd played with and fought with many years ago. They knew me too well as I had been. They knew my weaknesses. They knew me as no student should know his teacher!

I sat leafing through a thick textbook without seeing its pages. A warm dampness covered my face as the expectant silence fell upon the room. I wanted to run, to escape. I was a little girl, darting off with a stolen lunch bucket; I was the girl who had attacked a classmate for having soiled Mingie's new red socks; I was the girl who had once written a letter so foul that colored town must still be whispering about it. . . .

Somehow I had stepped down from the platform. I was standing close to the front row of desks.

"Good morning, class."

For a second I felt a blank surprise. That had been my own voice I had heard, and it had been clear and firm. I let out, silently, a long-held breath.

The greetings in response to mine were a mixture of Miss Bennetts and Veanies. Plainly, that would not do. A teacher can't very well have some of her students saying "Hey, Veanie" while the others are saying "Good morning, Miss Bennett."

"Hey, Veanie!" That was funny for a teacher and the head of the English department, and I had to smile just a little. But I said:

"Now, class, I know most of you and you know me. Some of you called me by my first name. Thank you. That gives me a warm feeling. Now I know that I've come home. But—" I paused to emphasize that important little word—"a teacher is a guide and director; a friend, too, but not in the old way as when we were playmates. I have been honored with a position I deeply respect, and you respect it too, or you wouldn't be here. Don't you think that it is fitting, in this new relationship between us, to call me Miss Bennett?"

I stopped and searched each face. Everyone nodded Yes but one man who had been in tenth grade with me. He just looked at me, and I didn't like that look at all.

"Thank you," I acknowledged the almost unanimous agreement. I stepped back to my desk and from one of its drawers took out a bundle of pencils and a stack of paper. I laid them on the desk of the man who had not nodded. "Will you please give each student a pencil and a sheet of paper for me?" I asked him.

There was a tense moment—no, hardly a moment; a split second, when I thought all was lost. Then, without a word, he rose and went about his task.

The whole thing had been a matter of minutes. I would never again have to go through that particular ordeal. I had come a long way, up a long hill, and up at the top had very nearly tumbled down. But—"It's all right, Veanie," I seemed to hear Miss Rossie's voice. "You've made it!"

My next class was a tenth-grade group. Mingie was in it.

Mingie had not got beyond the seventh grade before she married. Now that she was returning to school, the principal had judged that because of her age and her record she could start in tenth grade.

I gave a little talk to this class the same as I had to the seniors, and their response was entirely favorable. But there was Mingie sitting quietly in the back row and the students, now and again, could not help looking from their fellow classmate to the teacher, her twin. This too was something for which I was not prepared; and I was so happy to see Mingie in class that it was hard not to talk directly to her, and to her alone. But Mingie knew that right away. She raised her head and looked at me, and in that look was nothing but the respectful attention of a student to a teacher. To this day I don't understand how she did it, and how she maintained that attitude throughout. But I hope that I would have been the same if our positions had been reversed. I hope, but I wonder. . . .

At home, Mingie kept insisting: "Veanie, I don't care about high marks and I don't want you to give them to me. I just want to finish."

225

"But Mingie, honey, I've got to give you the mark you make—whatever it is, good or bad."

"It's just that I don't want them getting mad at you and saying you gave me a high mark because I'm your sister. You know how some people are."

"We can't help that," I said, thinking of many things in the past. "We never could, Mingie."

Yes, I knew how some people were. And if I hadn't, I would have found out that year; for I had my troubles—but practically always with the parents, seldom with the students.

There was a girl to whom I had to give a D in tenth-grade English. I certainly wished I hadn't had to; for her mother was one of the women I'd met near the railroad tracks that evening long ago—one of the three spreading the ugly gossip about me.

I knew I'd hear from her, and I did. "My daughter ain' no dumb chile, an' she better get more'n a D, or else. . . !" she threatened me. "You jus' tryin' to low-rate my girl 'cause you always been mad at me."

I saw she expected me to flare up, and that was what she wanted. Then she'd have something to go to the principal with. Years earlier, I would undoubtedly have lost my temper, but I'd learned my lesson. I told her that I was about to give out a test in English grammar, and I invited her to come to school and be with me when the examination papers were brought to me.

She did it and sat with me as I corrected each paper and showed it to her. She'd not had much schooling, yet it was enough to enable her to see how many mistakes her daughter had made.

"She ain' no dumb chile," the mother repeated, but without anger against me. She was only troubled now. "I see that gal jus' been playin' 'round. She oughta done more better than that."

I agreed and said that if we'd work together, I was sure her girl would do much better.

"I'll see 'bout her at home, you see 'bout her here," she charged me.

We both did, and the result was what we hoped.

Mingie studied hard. She earned the high marks I gave her, but they brought me no criticism because her marks were as high, or higher, in her other subjects. Besides, everybody liked Mingie. That helped me too, because the liking for Mingie was extended to me, her twin. A few students grumbled, however. They said we weren't really alike—that if Mingie were the teacher she wouldn't work them so hard and be so strict. At home and at Mrs. Lee's, we laughed a lot about that.

Two years later, at graduation, Mingie was named valedictorian. She tried to transfer that honor to a younger student, but the principal wouldn't have it. So with me on the platform behind her and Miss Rossie in the front row before her, Mingie gave the address for the graduating class. She did better—far better—than I had, eight years earlier.

Afterwards, everybody gathered about her, glad for her, congratulating her. I was so proud and happy; but no prouder or happier than Miss Rossie.

Miss Rossie had her arm about Mingie. "Now college, Mingie," she said. "College!"

In the fall Mingie went to college at Tallahassee—"coming along right behind me," as she had once promised. Timmy and Ted were quite grown now and they were wonderful, responsible children. Mingie could leave them with me. She did well her first year and even better in the second.

By that time, at home, I was keeping company with a young

man I'd known since we were children and who'd been far away—as far as Hawaii—for the last five years, but was back now for a short stay with his parents. It was to be short because he was going to live in California; in fact, on his way from Hawaii, he had stopped in Los Angeles and bought a little house there.

John asked me to marry him; I told him Yes. Loving him, I could not ask him to choose Florida instead of California. Much has been said of the similarities of the two states, but no one can say that the conditions are the same for Negroes. So I agreed to go to Los Angeles with him.

This happened during a visit we made to Mingie's college—and mine—to see a football game and, of course, to be with Mingie. I told her at once and she was delighted I was to marry John. She'd known him as long as I had. She always had liked him and she was as sure as I was that we were especially suited for each other. "Oh, Veanie, I'm so happy for you!" She hugged me and then she reminded me of what, with all my happiiness, made my heart heavy: "What about Miss Rossie?"

For California meant leaving Miss Rossie and Edie and Sonny Boy and Mr. Lee and leaving them not for a few months at a time and by a hundred miles or so, as when I went away to college, but leaving them perhaps "for good" and going three thousand miles away. In my misery at the thought of it, the lines of an Irish song assailed me—"It may be for long, and it may be forever!" When one went so far away, who could know? The dread that never again would I see Miss Rossie made the thought of California unbearable to me. Yet I knew that, out of her love for me, Miss Rossie would insist that I go.

I brought John to Miss Rossie. I surprised her because I'd never said anything about him. I hadn't been certain until the moment he had proposed; then I had known.

She liked John at once, and she saw we were in love.

"Veanie, I'm so happy for you," she said. "When will it be? Are you planning a wedding?"

"No, ma'am, Miss Rossie—just a marriage."

We all laughed at that, and a little tension drifted away. John had been secretly worried about meeting my adored Miss Rossie. I guess the build-up I'd been giving her had made her seem a little more than human.

Mr. Lee came in and was pleased with our news. He looked closely at John: "I believe I know you. Aren't you John Sams's son—the one who does cement work?"

"Yes, sir; he's my father."

Miss Rossie had me give John a cold drink out on the back porch, and she and Mr. Lee stood asking us questions about our trip.

Miss Rossie said, "I wish California weren't so far away. . . Mingie must be wishing that too."

"Mingie's coming out to us in California, Miss Rossie, as soon as she finishes college."

"Mingie too?" She sighed a little. "How I'll miss you! But you must go."

And then she was watching me, giving me worried little glances. She knew me so well; she knew what I was feeling. She took me to the bedroom and we talked.

She had made over the world for Mingie and me; but she had not, and she could not, make over John's world. She could do little for him if we stayed here, and she had just about reached the limit of what she could do for Mingie and me. With what she had given us we could go, by ourselves, much further in California.

All this she made plain to me. I cried a little, and there were tears in her eyes too. But we both knew that the time had come, as it does for so many mothers and daughters. She had prepared me well, and now it was time for me to go.

The morning came. John and I were packed and his car was waiting. We drove to Mrs. Lee's. She met us at the door.

"Come on in and have a cup of coffee and something to eat before you start," she said.

"Thank you, Miss Rossie," I said, "but we've had breakfast."

"You can drink a last cup of coffee with me—won't you? Mr. Lee has had his and gone. I thought I'd wait till you all came, to have mine. Come in and let John sit here on the porch while you heat it up."

While I went about turning on the stove and getting out the cups and saucers, John sat quietly in his chair, facing me through the door. A last cup of coffee with my Miss Rossie. . . a last cup. . . . A great loneliness engulfed me. John was looking at me and I saw the pain in his face; I smiled at him but not successfully.

I filled the cups while Mrs. Lee talked happily. "Veanie, what are you planning to do out there in Los Angeles? Are you going to work or are you going to let John do it all?"

"I'll try to get into teaching there as soon as possible," I said. "But I've heard that the qualifications are higher than here. So until I'm able to meet them I suppose I'll do something else—almost anything, just so it's work. I'd be uncomfortable doing nothing, Miss Rossie."

"Yes, that's like you." She smiled. "We've written references and recommendations for you. I'll get them—and I've something else for you, too." She rose and went into her bedroom.

She was humming when she returned with a big box. "This is only a little gift for your new home," she said.

230

It was no little gift. In the box was a pile of fine embroidered bed linen, folded neatly in tissue.

I sat there, looking at the box. John spoke for me, admiring the gift and thanking her for it. Then he went out to the car and left me with Miss Rossie.

I couldn't—I didn't want to, ever—take my eyes from that dear face.

"Miss Rossie, I wish you could just know how much you have meant to Mingie and me through all these years. I wish that I could—could only explain—" I managed that and could get no further, for I was crying so. "You—you just don't know—how—"

"Hush, now," Miss Rossie said. She put her arm about my waist and walked with me to the screen door. We looked at each other through our tears.

She touched my cheek. "You're a lovely girl, Veanie. You'll be happy."

I kissed her hand.

"Good-by, Veanie, honey. Be sweet and write as soon as you get home."

Home! It seemed I could not make my feet move. Something within me all but cried out: Home is here!

As our car moved off, I looked back at the graceful figure, still as a portrait on the screen; just so, Mrs. Lee has remained with me.

It was a long ride to California, and somewhere along the way John and I had our talk. Or rather, John said what, sooner or later, he had to say if we were to be close together:

"Veanie, I see why you feel as you do about Miss Rossie and I know how you're missing her, but Veanie, darling—" It was hard for him, I understood that, but it had to be said. A man who is in love with his wife cannot be happy when he sees her pining away, deeply in love with somebody else besides himself, even though that somebody else is another woman, not a man. I knew I must turn away from what was behind me and live for the dear man who was at my side. Yes, I knew that; but all the same I couldn't keep back a surge of resentment.

He said: "If all Florida were like her, California wouldn't be so much better for you and me; but it is, Veanie."

Still I wouldn't look at him. But from the corner of my eye I saw he wasn't looking at me, either. And then I saw a little smile on his face. "You know, Veanie," he said, "it's her smile —it's a way she has—the way she smiles. . . ."

And then it was all right.

22

WHEN WE REACHED HOME in Los Angeles—and now, in John's pretty house, I could say "home" and feel it—I could not rest until I had mailed letters to Mingie and to Miss Rossie. It was the beginning of a long, unfailing correspondence. In my letter to Miss Rossie about a month later, I told her how her glowing references had helped me to get jobs, among other places, in the homes of movie stars.

"I never dreamed I would be so near to a real live movie star," I wrote. "The first night I served a party, I almost dropped my tray on Rita Hayworth's shoulder because a resemblance to you startled me so."

Early in August I took a written examination for a school position. I was so eager to get back into teaching that I could hardly wait for the result of the test. But I had to wait, day after day, hoping and praying. John was hoping and praying in my behalf. He had a good job as an engine painter in an aircraft plant. Each evening when he came home, he asked if I'd had word yet, and then he'd comfort and reassure me that it was going to be all right. Way across the continent, in Florida, Miss Rossie was hoping and praying too. I'd written her about the test—and back had come a telegram telling me not to worry; of course I'd passed.

And at last I received formal notification that I *had* passed the written examination. I must now report, in two days, for the oral.

"The oral will be much harder," I said, already worrying. "And I know I ought to wait, but I just can't; I've got to wire Miss Rossie."

John agreed; so off went my telegram and back came another from Miss Rossie. I took it with me, as though it was a luck charm, when I went to the personnel building for the decisive ordeal.

Some may find it more trying to sit off alone and hour after hour write answers to printed questions. But it had always been hard for me to face strangers, and it was with no little fear that I began the half hour of the oral examination.

From the moment I entered the room, I knew I was under observation for appearance, bearing, and manner. I sat at a long table with the examiners—kindly enough but searching. They wanted to know everything about me, from when and where I was born to why I liked children. Very soon, among other things, they were learning about Mrs. Lee. And when I began to talk about her, my fears fell away. At the end I had a hunch they knew more about her and how wonderful she was than about me and my fitness for teaching.

By Friday or by Saturday, at the latest—I thought—I would hear from the board. But no letter came. Sunday was a bad day for me and for John. On Monday morning the telephone wakened me. A woman's voice told me I was to report to a school three blocks from my home and start work as a probationary teacher.

I was given a third-grade class composed of children of many nationalities and colors who played, worked, and shared together with no evidence of racial friction. I was enchanted with them. Oddly, my first problem was provided by two small Negro girls. They were sisters, but one was almost fair of skin and had long brown curls framing her plump, smooth face; the other was as black as ebony, with long, kinky braids, yet no less attractive than her sister.

It was the light-skinned little girl I found sulking against a wall while all the other children in the yard were playing.

"Are you ill, dear?" I asked her.

"No."

"Then join the other girls and play—"

"I don't want to play."

"But what's wrong?"

"It's—it's my sister—"

"Yes."

"She's black and the kids keep telling me she doesn't look like me, and ask me why she's so black. I don't want to see her."

So here it was after all—color prejudice, color frustration, stirring even between sisters. For a few moments I was speechless from my feeling of helplessness to deal with it. Then I remembered something. I did not attempt anything that day.

Before leaving home the next morning, I picked two bunches of flowers—one a cluster of solid pink dahlias, the other a bouquet of varicolored dahlias with gradient hues from dark purple to pale magenta, from deep rose to cerise. I arranged them in contrasting vases and placed them on my desk in the classroom.

As the children filed in, the flowers fascinated them, and many halted to touch and admire them before going to their seats.

I watched for the little girl who was ashamed of her sister and, when she stopped before the vases, I asked her which she liked best.

"Those!"—and she promptly pointed to the mixed bouquet.

"Will you wait here, dear," I asked her. "For we aren't going to keep both bunches of flowers—only the one the class likes better. The other, we'll give to the office because they like to have it look pretty, too. I'm going to ask the children to vote for the one we want to keep; and will you count for me when they hold up their hands?"

The vote went almost unanimously for the variegated bouquet.

I asked one of the little boys to tell the class why he liked it better.

"Because they're so many colors," he replied, and the other children, in answer to my question, said the same.

"Yes. I like these, too," I agreed. "We all like variety. God likes it, too. That must be why he made so many beautiful colors for us to enjoy. And He made not only flowers of different colors; He made yellow people, white people, brown people, black people, and red people and put us all together in the world as we plant flowers of all colors in our gardens. The world is His garden; and He loves us all. He wanted us to be different or He wouldn't have made us so. And it's certain, when He looks down on us to bless us, He doesn't see just the color of our skins; He looks into our hearts to find if they are clean and good, to see if we have good thoughts and deeds there. . . ."

Later I was praised for my handling of that situation. It wasn't I who'd handled it, but Miss Rossie in me.

Mingie came to California, bringing her boys with her. She had finished three years of college, taking elementary classroom teaching, as I had. But now she decided to change;

she was going to be a nurse. Mingie had never forgotten Papa and his tragic bedridden days. It was as a nurse that she would give herself to others.

Miss Rossie received more telegrams and specials that year than ever before in her life. Mingie and I wrote or bulletined everything we were doing. Never—not once—did Miss Rossie fail to make a prompt reply.

Upon completing her training, Mingie immediately was placed in one of the city's largest hospitals.

So often we talked about Miss Rossie, Mingie and I. How we missed her! We would see her soon, we kept saying to each other. But "soon" is like the Mexican "mañana"; the trouble with soon is that it has no definiteness.

The years went by. In Florida, Edie married; and in California, Mingie's Teddy, and then Tim. In Florida, Sonny Boy married. In California, Mingie married again. Telegrams and letters flew back and forth.

"Veanie," Mingie said, "you know, I have a funny feeling about Miss Rossie." She had in her hand a letter she'd just received. "She doesn't say so but I don't think she's well."

"She'd never say so." I voiced what we both knew. "She wouldn't want us to worry about her; and she'd never, never complain. I wish we could go out there."

"It takes a lot of money from here to Florida."

"Yes, but I've been saving up. I'll write her tonight and tell her I'll be coming soon."

"Soon."

But Mr. Lee's telegram came first:

MRS. LEE VERY ILL CAN YOU COME

The slowing train screeches to a stop and begins to back around the weed-fringed curve to the station. It is dark but as I sit on the edge of my seat, peering out, the surroundings are so familiar; there has been little change since I was here, years ago.

Beside the wooden platform, a few white cabmen stand at ease or lean against lampposts, leisurely puffing on their cigarettes. In spite of my years in Los Angeles, I do not attempt to engage any of them. As I step from the train, I look for, and find, a colored taxi. I recognize the driver; he is very old now. I hope he won't know me; I do not want to talk.

I speak to him and he doesn't know me. I give him the address. "You sure, lady?" he asks. "Ain't that up in the white section?"

"Yes. That's where I want to go, please."

"All right, Miss—if that's where you wanta go," he says, his tone foreboding.

Royal Palm Avenue seems unbearably quiet and lonely, although what had been vacant plots are now occupied by homes, and windows are glowing in the night.

How many times had Mingie and I walked that street, to and from Mrs. Lee's? How many times had we sought that special haven? I cannot bear to think of her house without her; but I warn myself again—her beautiful life is coming to its end.

Her life! Into my mind comes the first line of a little book I opened one day in the college library. It was not a religious book; it was by the archaeologist Flinders Petrie. It started with the simple, tremendous statement: "The meaning of Life has in all ages been the goal of human thought."

I cannot even attempt to say what is its meaning, but I have no difficulty in describing what it was that gave one life—Miss Rossie's—its meaning. It was love.

Yet, there are many kinds of love, just as there are many varieties of prejudice and hate. Love can be greedy, or tyrannical, selfish, demanding, even cruel. Miss Rossie's love had none of these elements. Never did it cling, hurt, or drain. It strengthened, supported, healed.

The great trunks of the royal palms are light gray beside the white walk, and I look high over their soaring fronds, realizing how much they have grown in the years; the magnolias, too.

The cab has gone and still I stand before the house. The garden is luminous in the soft sweet light of the full summer moon. "How pretty your flowers are growing." I know from the heaviness of the air that the day has been sultry, though the night is cool.

I bow my head and try to pray: My Lord, my God, don't let her suffer—be good to her—I cannot go on even silently, to myself, but now I am able to move. I mount the steps and put a finger to the bell, but withdraw it; instead, I rap softly on the door.

It opens a crack and I see a middle-aged, blond woman I do not know. "Yes?" she asks. "Who is it?"

"This—this is Veanie."

"Oh, yes—come in, Veanie. She's been wanting to see you."

I set down my bag. The woman closes the door and cautions: "Everybody is there in her room. You wait here."

"But, ma'am, can't I go in?"

"I don't know. I'll go and see."

She disappears down the familiar hallway. But here, suddenly, is Mr. Lee. "Hello, Veanie."

He is not the same Mr. Lee I remember on the day before I drove off to California. His face is pale and worn; his eyes, always so cheerful and gay, are desperately sad. His tone is strange—low and hoarse. He gives me a hand that has no grip, and with the other brushes back his hair, as thick as ever but now nearly pure white. "She won't know you now. She has been in a coma since yesterday."

I can scarcely speak at all; after each word, I have to swallow. "Can—can I—go in—now?"

"Yes. Come on in, Veanie."

The bedroom was always spacious, but I see it has been enlarged and remodeled. An air conditioner at a window hums dreamily, and it alone disturbs the silence. The scent of roses fills the air from the vases on the dressing table. As I step in, I have the familiar feel of deep-napped carpet beneath my feet.

The nurse moves aside and my eyes settle upon the bed. There is a faint rise and fall of the blue bed jacket; but the still face shows no awareness of my presence.

There is weariness upon it and the soft brown hair now is white at the temples. But somehow she seems more girllike than I had ever seen her, and more beautiful.

I look up for a moment into the grief-stricken faces of Edie and Sonny Boy. They are married now and have children of their own, and I scarcely know them. But there is something of her in each of them, and it will go on and on; and it will go on—please, God—in California, where her black twin "daughters" and her black "grandchildren" live and carry in their hearts the meaning of this one, ebbing life.

I bow my head in prayer. When I open my eyes, I see, among the vases on her dressing table, neat stacks of letters tied with ribbons bleached by time. Mingie's letters and mine.

I look up at Mr. Lee and he nods. He steps away a little and I follow him. He tells me about the letters. He had not known that she had kept them until, a few days ago, she had told him they were in the bottom of the cedar chest and begged him to get them out. And so he had placed them on her dressing table where she could see them.

There is a slight stir on the bed. The throat ripples a little; the eyelids open, but close again. Taking the pallid wrist between her fingers, the nurse glances at Mr. Lee. Then she places the soft, limp arm on the sheet—and waits.

There is the glow of a tender smile. There is a faint expulsion of breath. The pillow sinks a little.

As sweetly as she had lived, she went to rest. I say to myself, God needed more kindness and love in Heaven.

ABOUT THE AUTHOR

Jessie Bennett Sams—Veanie in the book—is today a teacher in the elementary school system in Los Angeles, where she has worked for ten years. She was born in Alachua, Florida, educated at Florida A. & M. College in Tallahassee, and did graduate work at the University of Southern California and the University of Colorado. When not teaching, she not only writes but paints and has worked extensively in ceramics.

Of *White Mother* Mrs. Sams writes: "It was not at first intended to be an autobiography, but I found that I could do it no other way and still reveal and convey my full purpose—to write the story of a most gracious lady—a Southern white lady—to whom my sister and I attribute all that is sweet in our lives. I discovered that my sister and I were so intricately woven into the background, setting, and the story itself that we had to fulfill our inherent parts in this beautiful memory. Thus I ventured to tell the story as we lived it then and remember it now."